M'Kee
Victorian Glass

FIVE COMPLETE GLASS CATALOGS
FROM 1859/60 TO 1871

by

M'Kee and Brothers

With an Introduction and Text by
Lowell Innes
and
Jane Shadel Spillman

THE CORNING MUSEUM OF GLASS, CORNING
IN ASSOCIATION WITH
DOVER PUBLICATIONS, INC., NEW YORK

DEDICATION

Our appreciation of and gratitude to The Corning Museum of Glass! Its wealth of material is available to researchers and a helpful staff is always willing to assist.

Published in Canada by General Publishing Company, Ltd., 30 Lesmill Road, Don Mills, Toronto, Ontario.
Published in the United Kingdom by Constable and Company, Ltd., 10 Orange Street, London WC2H 7EG.

M'Kee Victorian Glass: Five Complete Glass Catalogs from 1859/60 to 1871 is a new work, first published by Dover Publications, Inc., in 1981. The catalog of 1871 is reproduced from an original in the Smithsonian Institution Libraries.

International Standard Book Number: 0-486-24121-1
Library of Congress Catalog Card Number: 80-69671

Manufactured in the United States of America
Dover Publications, Inc.
180 Varick Street
New York, N.Y. 10014

INTRODUCTION

IN the mid nineteenth century the glass industry was actively expansive. The steady improvement in furnaces, presses, molds, and working tools, already instituted, was continuing. The perfection of the soda-lime formula in 1864 by William Leighton of Hobbs Brockunier, Wheeling, had put table glass within reach of every household. But expansion of the market brought fierce competition—designs were copied, altered, adapted, even directly pirated. Therefore, a study of company catalogs, besides offering the obvious advantage of pinpointing a starting date of a pattern, documents the original pattern as well. Careful students of pressed glass have long wished that early patterns could be identified more accurately. Though the design section of the Patent Office was opened in 1842, the earliest patent for pressed-glass design patterns was not registered till April 1, 1863, by Frederick M'Kee of M'Kee and Brothers, Pittsburgh, for Sprig (Ribbed Palm).

Four catalogs of the M'Kee glass company of Pittsburgh, dating from ca. 1860 to 1871, and an undated Price List, ca. 1863, are here made available for study in the hope that reprinting these catalogs for collectors and including an analysis of each will provide a useful research tool to stimulate further scholarship. The catalog of ca. 1860 has been in the library of The Corning Museum of Glass for a number of years and has never been reprinted. The 1864 catalog bears the autograph of Frederick McKee on its cover and with the Price List was owned by Lowell Innes for many years. (Although Frederick McKee signed his name with that spelling, all four printed catalogs consistently use M'Kee.) The 1868 catalog has been partially reprinted several times, by Ruth Webb Lee, A. C. Revi, and Sandra Stout; the copy they used is now in The Corning Museum of Glass library. The 1871 catalog belongs to the library of the Smithsonian Institution and is reprinted here with their permission.

The M'Kee firm was very important in the Pittsburgh glass industry. It had started in 1854 as F. and J. M'Kee, changed its name to M'Kee and Brother in 1860, and to M'Kee and Brothers in 1863 or 1864, when Stewart M'Kee joined the firm. At the time of the major strike of November 1878, the factory employed 160 hands and had a weekly payroll of $2,000. Except for James B. Lyon's O'Hara Glass Works, it was the largest tableware factory in Pittsburgh at that time.

This series of closely dated catalogs enables us to examine changes in the glass industry at a critical period: the soda-lime formula had been introduced, large sets of matching tableware in pressed glass became a market staple, and kerosene became the favorite fuel for lighting. Glass-factory catalogs are rare, and it is most unusual to have access to four from one factory covering a single decade. We have no similar evidence for more famous factories such as the Boston & Sandwich Glass Company and the New England Glass Company.

Before analyzing the M'Kee catalogs, we should examine the scanty documentary evidence that exists from before 1860. The Patent Office is a reliable source, even if the design section was not used widely for pattern glass. Joseph Magoun of the New England Glass Company registered three patents for purposes other than design, but in each case the patent drawing shows an unmistakable relationship to a New England Glass Company pattern. On September 24, 1847, Magoun patented a lamp. In the patent illustration the font carried loops in the style of the New England Glass Company Loop. His patent of September 25, 1847, concerned the joining and fashioning of the stem and font of a goblet. The patent drawings show the bowl of the goblet in the famous New England Glass Company Flute pattern. On October 24, 1848, Magoun patented a mold for producing *incavo* ornaments on the exterior surface of the glassware.[1] The tumbler pictured in the drawing carried the Ashburton pattern, another early design of the New England Glass Company.

Lura Woodside Watkins, in an article based on a New England Glass Company catalog of ca. 1869, listed bills and invoices covering glass shipped to California. One, dated January 28, 1851, speaks of "Splendid Ashburton Celery Vases Scalloped," to be sold at $2.50 each.[2] Undoubtedly the shipment was meant for the Forty-Niners.

In A. C. Revi's *American Pressed Glass and Figure Bottles*, the author shows a page from an undated Bryce, Richards & Co. catalog,

[1] Lura W. Watkins. "Pressed Glass of the New England Glass Company—An Early Catalogue at The Corning Museum," *Journal of Glass Studies*, 12, 1970, p. 158.
[2] *Ibid.*, p. 159.

Pittsburgh.[3] Since the partnership existed from 1854 to 1865, it is safe to assume that the catalog was printed in those years. Nine pieces of pressed pattern glassware illustrated patterns; clearly delineated are Tulip and Sawtooth, Diamond Point, and Harp. The others are variants or adaptations. A Curling, Robertson & Co. (Fort Pitt) advertisement in the Pittsburgh-Allegheny Directory of 1856–1857 shows Waffle and Thumbprint (Midwestern version), Flute, and Colonial.[4]

One other catalog should be considered before we study the five sequential M'Kee catalogs. Henry L. Ringwalt, formerly a partner in Curling, Robertson & Co. of Pittsburgh, had left the firm to become a manufacturer's agent, probably in 1858. He lists his 1860 offerings as *Second Annual Catalogue*.[5]

One catalog page pictures 155 pieces of glass, an amazing display of various forms in the pressed patterns offered: Huber, 45; Cincinnati (Honeycomb), 38; Crystal, 14; O'Hara, 10; and Genella, 6. Only two pieces, a cut water bottle and an engraved one, hark back to earlier techniques. Of the 155 pieces, 35 are pressed tumblers, quite in keeping with the percentage found in other catalogs.

The Ringwalt catalog establishes the variety of forms existing in pressed tablewares by 1860, and it clearly emphasizes the plainness and simplicity of designs produced 15 years before the Centennial.

Names of pressed patterns found in early advertising are not always definitive. Huber varies little from factory to factory. But three different versions of Honeycomb were available. New York, in which the pattern covers only the lower half of each piece, is offered by M'Kee in 1864, 1868, and 1871; by Bakewell, Pears & Co., ca. 1875; by King, Sons & Co., ca. 1875; and by the New England Glass Company in 1869. Cincinnati, in which the pattern covered the whole object, was advertised by Ringwalt in 1860 and was made by J. B. Lyon before 1861; Vernon, in which the pattern covers all but a narrow rim at the top, appears in the New England Glass Company catalog of 1869, and in M'Kee's 1868 and 1871 catalogs where it is called Cincinnati. In his folder, Ringwalt names two different patterns Crystal, a practice M'Kee repeats with two different patterns called Argus. O'Hara is the J. B. Lyon and Company's name for the New England Glass Company's Loop, and Leaf is the M'Kee name for a very similar pattern.

[3] A. C. Revi. *American Pressed Glass and Figure Bottles*, New York: Thomas Nelson & Sons, 1963, p. 80.
[4] Lowell Innes. *Pittsburgh Glass 1797–1891. A History and Guide for Collectors*, Boston: Houghton Mifflin Company, 1976, p. 304.
[5] *Ibid.*, p. 309.

BIBLIOGRAPHY

Bakewell, Pears & Co. Catalog, ca. 1875. Pittsburgh, privately printed by Thomas C. Pears III, 1977.

Chipman, Frank W. *The Romance of Old Sandwich Glass*. Sandwich Publishing Co., Inc., 1932.

Davis, Pearce. *The Development of the American Glass Industry*. New York: Russell & Russell, 1949.

Innes, Lowell. *Pittsburgh Glass 1797–1891 A History and a Guide for Collectors*. Boston: Houghton-Mifflin, 1976.

Keyes, Homer Eaton. "By No Means Sandwich." *Antiques*, April 1927, Vol. 11, No. 4, pp. 284–286.

King, Son, & Co. *Illustrated Catalogue, Crystal Glassware, Cascade Glass Works*. Pittsburgh: [1875].

Lee, Ruth Webb. *Early American Pressed Glass*. Wellesley Hills: Lee Publications, 1946.

Revi, A. C. *American Pressed Glass and Figure Bottles*. New York: Thomas Nelson & Sons, 1963.

Stout, Sandra. *The Complete Book of McKee Glass*. North Kansas City: Trojan Press, 1972.

Stow, Charles Messer. "Sandwich Glass That Pittsburgh Made." *Antiquarian* 13, Oct. 1929, pp. 46, 47.

Thuro, Catherine M. V. *Oil Lamps: The Kerosene Era in North America*. Des Moines: Wallace-Homestead Book Co., 1976.

Watkins, Lura Woodside. "Pressed Glass of the New England Glass Company—An Early Catalogue at the Corning Museum." *Journal of Glass Studies*, 12 1970, pp. 149–164.

THE 1859/60 CATALOG

THE first M'Kee catalog has been dated for us by Mrs. G. S. Cunningham of the Pennsylvania Room in the Carnegie Library at Pittsburgh. Using Pittsburgh City Directories, she found the following entries:

    1859/60   Haven, W. S., printers, Corner of Market & Second
    1860/61   Haven, W. S., Wood and Third. (This listing continued through 1873)

    1858/59   M'Kee, F. & J., 23 Wood St.
    1859/60   M'Kee, F. & Bro., 23 Wood St.

Since the catalog in The Corning Museum of Glass is from M'Kee & Brother, successors to F. & J. M'Kee, and since W. S. Haven, Corner of Market & Second Streets, printed it, we may conclude that it was published before the spring of 1860 and after the spring of 1859, when F. & J. M'Kee ceased to be the firm name.

The 1860 catalog has a limited emphasis on sets. There are two ways to judge the patterns: by noting those listed in the price guide and by recording the number of shapes actually pictured in each pattern. Only three patterns show more than eight items—Excelsior, Eugenie, and Crystal. Of the many patterns listed, only four had six or more forms: Leaf (Loop), Flute, Mitre Diamond and Ray.

In studying tableware forms such as decanters, pitchers (including creamers), sugars, eggcups and celery glasses, there are three names (Excelsior, Eugenie, Crystal) that appear regularly but not consistently. No Eugenie decanter appears, for instance; no Excelsior celery is listed or pictured; no Eugenie pitcher is recorded. Crystal is the only pattern chosen for a cross section with an example in every class.

These three patterns well exemplify the plain and geometric style of early pressing. Their relationship to the styles of earlier cut glass is clearly discerned. Early pressed-glass designers probably wanted to soften the rigidity of cut glass. Thus, Excelsior and Eugenie employ curving lines against geometric figures.

Modern students of nineteenth-century pattern glass generally, perhaps unwillingly, believe that *large* sets of pressed tableware were not available until the middle sixties, although some patterns were available in more than one form as early as the late 1840s—about the beginning for what is today called "pressed-pattern glass." Because of the variety of products pictured, it seems that the M'Kees were testing the market for future production. Medical instruments, lanterns, toys, specie jars, retorts, tinctures with ground crown stoppers, druggists' wares, and household articles are all shown.

A study of J. B. Lyon's 1861 catalog (O'Hara Flint Glass Works) shows a sharp contrast.[6] After the two first pages of tumblers and the next one of goblets, the rest of the catalog is devoted to forms of pressed tableware. Obviously, Lyon had selected his area of specialization.

The Price Guide attached to the M'Kee 1860 catalog shows us that no other pieces of Comet will be found except the 6" covered compote and the 6" covered and/or uncovered nappie. Two styles of Argus appear—the so-called Thumbprint produced by Bakewell and a slightly different Argus pattern reproduced for the Henry Ford Museum several years ago. The slight changes in a popular basic pattern like Diamond are listed as Mitre Diamond, Scallop Diamond, and Diamond and Circle. This sort of adaptation or alteration was going on all the time. Our printed list of patterns pictured will enable a collector to correlate the design with the number of forms in which it was originally shown. Many patterns appear in only two or three forms.

The names of the patterns are sometimes descriptive (Diamond and Circle, Mitre Diamond) and sometimes, perhaps, topical. The Eugenie pattern was probably named after the French Empress Eugénie (crowned 1853), consort of Napoleon III. The Lind tumbler may have been named for Jenny Lind, the Swedish Nightingale, who was popular in the 1850s. The Comet pattern resembles a comet but whether it was inspired by a particular celestial body is not known. Halley's Comet had last appeared in 1835 and no particularly spectacular comets of the late 1850s are known to modern astronomers. Tumblers

[6] Innes, *op. cit.*, p. 305.

were also named after cities (New Orleans, Charleston, Philadelphia) as well as after people.

Only four candlesticks are in the picture section: French, Boston, Dolphin, and 6 Flute. The M'Kee French is quite unlike the Tulip No. 54 in the Ringwalt flyer.[7] The Boston is similar to Bakewell's Thistle,[8] and the 6 Flute has all the severity of line popular in the fifties. The Dolphin should be carefully compared with Eastern sticks carrying a round base. No Excelsior stick is listed or pictured, but we know such sticks are in several collections. Accordingly, we cannot consider a catalog as the last word.

The catalog contains one 3″ Diamond cup plate listed as such. The fact that only one cup plate is shown probably indicates that cup plates were going out of fashion at this time. However, this same 3″ plate is shown in 1864, 1868, and 1871, but is referred to merely as a 3″ plate in the Diamond pattern. There must have been some buyers for it, or it wouldn't have stayed in the catalog. Doubtless people who were set in their ways continued to use cup plates whether they were fashionable or not. As a matter of terminology, it should be noted that, although M'Kee was still selling the plate, it was not called a cup plate, perhaps because there wasn't much other use for such an item.

A number of salt dishes appear in the earliest catalog and most of those shown reappear throughout the decade. There are a Concave salt, Tulip and Lotus salts, individual salt (the only individual salt shown, although cut ones could be ordered), a Fillmore salt (probably named after the President), a Mason salt, a Rope salt, a Tomato salt, and an Imperial salt. Considering that all of these salts were available for a number of years, it is remarkable that so few of them appear in modern collections. Only the Imperial salt (also shown in the Bakewell catalog of ca. 1875)[9] will be familiar to collectors today.

Toy flatirons and toy candlesticks are also listed in all of these catalogs. For many years attributed to the Boston & Sandwich Glass Company, these toys are also on a Price List of the Cape Cod Glass Company in Sandwich, and it is likely that they were made at all three factories and at others as well. However, the M'Kee catalog is the only one to illustrate the toy flatirons and candlesticks which may be found by modern collectors. The M'Kee catalogs do not show the variety of lacy miniature tureens, washbowl sets, cups and saucers, and pitchers which are found in the East, and it is possible that these lacy mini-

---

[7] Innes, *op. cit.*, p. 59.
[8] *Bakewell, Pears and Company Catalogue*, ca. 1875. Privately printed by Thomas C. Pears III, 1977, p. 21.
[9] *Ibid.*, p. 28.

atures were never made in the Midwest. Toy table sets as well as children's mugs and plates were shown in a catalog of King, Son & Co., ca. 1875, and offered by Doyle & Company in 1876.[10]

The objects pictured in the catalogs under "Sundries and Household Ware" remained fairly constant through the decade. Here one finds butter prints, the stamps for making a design on homemade butter, birdbaths and seed boxes for bird cages, fountains for bird cages, and glass eggs for nesting hens or for darning. There are also ring jars, soap dishes, inkstands, nursing bottles, and other household ware, including a glass drawer knob. According to the Price List, fish globes were available, made to order in any size, and also shoemakers' globes which were cheaper and therefore probably smaller. The so-called lacemakers' lamps are not listed, but lacemaking was primarily a European industry. Julep tubes were also available, but since they were not pictured we do not know what they were. Items like these probably were made at every factory in the country, and it is rarely possible, even with the pictures given in the catalog, to make much of a positive attribution.

One of the things that makes these catalogs so fascinating is that they help to trace the evolution of lamp fuels. In the earliest catalog there are 24 cut shades which must have been used on Argand, astral, or solar lamps of various types. In contrast, there are only three chimneys available, all for solar lamps, a couple of plain blown shades and two lanterns, which are listed as available for both oil and for candles. Oil presumably means whale oil or lard oil since this was a Midwestern firm. There is also one gas shade. Gas as a fuel was not readily available because of the piping involved, although several large cities did supply gas to householders. Most of the above-mentioned wares are all blown, not pressed, glass, and the cut shades required much hand decoration. These must have been shades used primarily in the city of Pittsburgh; country people are thought to have used plainer lamps.

There were a number of lamps available: a patent peg lamp and a Leaf (Loop) pattern lamp, both of which burned oil; a small night lamp which was listed for fluid, that is, burning fluid or camphene; and several large fluid lamps. The Price List indicated that all of the lamps could be had with burners for either burning fluid or oil. There was one coal-oil lamp listed in the 1860 catalog, and it is illustrated with its own chimney in use. There are no chimneys listed for the oil or fluid lamps because, as a general rule, they were not used. Coal oil, refined from coal, was to be replaced shortly by kerosene, the

[10] Innes, *op. cit.*, pp. 53, 301.

process of refining kerosene having been just discovered in 1859. Coal oil and kerosene do not burn very well without a chimney to increase the draft, unlike whale oil or burning fluid, both of which burned better with chimneys but were commonly used without them.

To summarize, the lamps listed for sale in 1859/60 were: Harp, Plain, Leaf (oil only), L & C (fluid only), Eugenie (fluid only), Night, Gaines, Star, Turnip stand lamp (coal oil), Turnip peg lamp (oil or fluid), Turnip hand lamp (oil or fluid). Only four of these lamps are pictured, but all are offered in the Price List and were available with wicks for fluid or oil. A collector researching any pattern in these catalogs should study the Price Lists as well as the illustrated pages. This catalog offers Bacon's burners, a patent burner for burning without a chimney, as a substitution for the regular burners. Unfortunately, the illustration does not show exactly what Bacon's burners were.

In addition to the blown shades, blown syrup jugs and molasses cans with molded patterns were also available. It is difficult to tell in some cases whether the ware illustrated was meant to be mold-blown or pressed, but it seems obvious that there was a persistence of mold blowing, especially for pillar-molded patterns, throughout the 1860s.

PICTURED IN THE 1859/60 CATALOG

PATTERN	NUMBER OF PIECES	PATTERN	NUMBER OF PIECES
Argus —3 Type 1	4	Flute, Small (condiment bottles)	3
—1 Type 2		French	1
Band	4		
Bigler	1	Gaines	4
		Gauche	1
Charleston	4	Gothic	1
Circle and Oval	2		
Comet	3	Harp	5
Concave	2	H.S.	4
Crystal	17		
Diamond	1	Leaf	6
Diamond & Circle	2	Lind	2
Diamond, Mitre	6	Lotus	1
Dolphin	1	Mioton	5
Eugenie	14	Mitre	1
Excelsior	15	Number 14	1
Fairy	1	Number 17 (condiment bottles)	3
Fillmore	1		
Flute (includes tumblers)	16	Plain	4

PATTERN	NUMBER OF PIECES	PATTERN	NUMBER OF PIECES
Ray	8	Shell	3
Ribbed	1	Star	4
Ribbed, Fine	1	Scallops, Diamond	1
Rope	1	Tulip	2
Rose	3	Turnip	2
R. & R. Pillared	1		

PRICES

OF

GLASS WARE

MANUFACTURED BY

M'KEE & BROTHER,

Successors to F. & J. M'Kee,

No. 23 Wood Street, between First & Second Sts.

PITTSBURGH, PA.

W. S. Haven, Book and Job Printer,
CORNER OF MARKET AND SECOND STREETS.

PRICES

OF

GLASS WARE

MANUFACTURED BY

M'KEE & BROTHER,

SUCCESSORS TO

F. & J. M'KEE,

No. 23 Wood Street, between First and Second Streets,

PITTSBURGH, PA.

PITTSBURGH:

PRINTED BY W. S. HAVEN, (CORNER OF MARKET AND SECOND STREETS.)

As we have our Glass put up by experienced packers, in the most neat and careful manner, we make no allowance for breakage, Bills of Lading being guarantee of good order when shipped.

DO YOU WISH TO HAVE YOUR GOODS INSURED?

We have an open Policy, covering shipments to all points, at as low rates as can be secured here, and include the premium in your regular merchandise account. Please say INSURE in all cases where you want the goods covered by us.

M'KEE & BROTHER'S

PRICE LIST.

TUMBLERS.

	Rough Bott'ms	Ground Bott'ms.
Pressed ½ Gill, Toy .... per doz. $	20	
Pressed ½ Pint, 6 Flute........ "	87	1 00
Pressed ⅓ Quart, 6 Flute,........ "	1 20	1 33
Pressed Pint, 6 Flute........ "	1 60	1 75
Pressed ⅓ Pint, Excelsior Footed........ "		1 33
Pressed ⅓ Quart, Excelsior Footed........ "		1 60
Pressed ⅓ Pint, Excelsior Ship........ "		1 00
Pressed ⅓ Quart, Excelsior Ship........ "		1 33
Pressed ½ Pint, Concave Flute........ "	1 20	1 33
Pressee ⅓ Quart, Mudge........ "	1 20	1 33
Pressed ⅓ Pint, Charleston........ "	80	90
Pressed ½ Pint, Charleston .... "	95	1 10
Pressed ⅓ Pint, Lind........ "	60	
Pressed ⅓ Quart, Band Footed .... "		1 60
Pressed ⅓ Quart, Star........ "	1 20	1 33
Pressed ⅓ Quart, Gaines........ "	1 20	1 33
Pressed ½ Pint, Crystal........ "		1 33
Pressed ⅓ Pint, 9 Flute Light........ "	53	
Pressed ½ Pint, 9 Flute Light........ "	66	
Pressed ⅓ Pint, 6 Flute........ "	60	
Pressed ½ Pint, Eugenie Footed .... "		1 33
Pressed ½ Pint, Lind........ "	66	
Pressed ⅓ Pint, Finger Flute .... "	70	83
Pressed ½ Pint, Finger Flute........ "	95	1 10
Pressed ⅓ Quart, Finger Flute .... "	1 20	1 33
Pressed ⅓ Pint, Bigler Flute........ "	72	85
Pressed ½ Pint, Bigler Flute........ "	95	1 10
Pressed Galvanic Battery, 3½ by 4 inches........ "		3 0C
Pressed Temperance........ "		5 0

5

MOLASSES CANS.

Pressed Pint Pillar Molasses Pitchers, Metal Tops	per doz.	$6 67
Pressed Excelsior Molasses Cans, Metal Tops	"	4 70
Pressed Excelsior Molasses Cans, Tin Tops	"	3 00
Pressed No. 14 Molasses Cans, Metal Tops	"	4 50
Pressed No. 14 Molasses Cans, Tin Tops	"	3 00
Pressed Rose Molasses Cans, Metal Tops	"	5 00
Pressed Rose Molasses Cans, Tin Tops	"	3 70
Pressed Cone Pillar Molasses Cans, Metal Tops	"	6 00
Pressed Cone Pillar Molasses cans, Tin Tops	"	4 70
Pressed Pint Fine Ribbed Molasses Cans, Glass Stoppers	"	1 20
Pressed Diamond Molasses Cans, Tin Tops	"	3 70
Pressed Diamond Molasses Cans, Metal Tops	"	5 00

CANDLESTICKS.

Pressed French, no Sockets	per doz.	$2 00
Pressed Boston, with Sockets	"	4 00
Pressed Dolphin, with Sockets	"	4 00
Pressed Dolphin, no Sockets	"	3 60
Pressed 6 Flute, no Sockets	"	2 50

CELERY GLASSES.

Pressed Ray	per doz.	$5 33
Pressed Eugenie	"	4 50
Pressed Crystal	"	6 00

SWEETMEATS, Footed, with Covers.

Pressed 7 inch Leaf and Covers	per doz.	$4 70
Pressed 7½ inch Tulip and Covers	"	5 00
Pressed 5½ inch Tulip and Covers	"	3 00
Pressed 6½ inch Harp and Covers	"	3 50
Pressed 6 inch Comet and Covers	"	3 70

SMOKE BELLS.

Plain White	per doz.	$ 8 00
Blue Edge	"	10 00
Red Edge	"	12 00

A2

4

BAR TUMBLERS.

	Rough Bott'ms.	Ground Bott'ms.
	per doz. $ 54	$ 66
Pressed Gill 6 Flute Bar	54	66
Pressed ½ Pint 6 Flute Foster Bar		1 20
Pressed Pint 6 Flute Bar	2 65	2 80
Pressed Pint 6 Flute Bar	54	66
Pressed Gill Plain Bar	87	1 00
Pressed ½ Pint Plain Bar	1 20	1 33
Pressed ½ Pint Plain Bar	87	1 00
Pressed ½ Pint Plain Saloon Bar		1 33
Pressed English Punch	80	93
Pressed ½ Pint 9 Flute Bar	93	1 06
Pressed ½ Pint 9 Flute Bar		1 33
Pressed ½ Pint 9 Flute Bar, extra Heavy	80	93
Pressed ½ Pint New York Bar	93	1 06
Pressed ½ Pint New Orleans Bar		1 20
Pressed ¾ Pint Gothic Bar		1 25
Pressed ¾ Pint Gauche Bar		1 33
Pressed ¾ Pint Mioton Bar	72	85
Pressed Gill Crystal Bar	87	1 00
Pressed ½ Pint Crystal Bar		

JELLY GLASSES.

Pressed Excelsior	per doz.	$1 30
Pressed 6 Flute Jelly Cups, Footed	"	1 00
Pressed 10 Flute Jelly Tumblers	"	95

PRESSED PLATES.

3 inch Diamond Cup	per doz.	16
6 inch Diamond Butter	"	60
6 inch Ray Butter	"	68

PRESSED CASTOR BOTTLES.

Swell Flute	per doz.	60
No. 17	"	66
Eugenie	"	70

PITCHERS AND CREAMS.

Pressed Large Quart Excelsior,......per doz.	$5 33
Pressed Large Pint Excelsior,.... "	4 00
Pressed Large Quart Gaines.... "	5 33
Pressed Large Quart Concave,.... "	5 33
Pressed ½ Pint Plain Creams.... "	1 30
Pressed Eugenie Creams.... "	3 00
Pressed Quart Ribbed Pitchers.... "	3 50
Pressed Quart Crystal Pitchers,.... "	8 00
Pressed ½ Quart Crystal Creams,.... "	3 00
Pressed Quart Plain Ring Pitchers,.... "	5 50

CHAMPAGNE GLASSES.

Pressed Excelsior.....per doz.	$1 60
Pressed H. S..... "	1 65
Pressed Diamond.... "	2 00
Pressed Eugenie.... "	1 75
Pressed 6 Flute,.... "	1 50
Pressed Crystal,.... "	1 75
Pressed Argus,.... "	1 75
Pressed Mioton Hotel,.... "	1 75

SYRUP CANS AND BOTTLES.

Pressed Pint Pillar Syrup Cans,.....per doz.	$4 00
Pressed Pint Pillar Syrup Bottles,.... "	3 00
Pressed Pint Fluted Syrup Cans,.... "	3 00
Pressed Pint Fluted Syrup Bottles,.... "	2 50

LANTERNS—Spring Bottoms.

Cone Flute, Oil or Candle.....per doz.	$5 75
No. 2 Pear, Oil or Candle.... "	6 00
No. 3 Pear, Oil or Candle.... "	8 00
Cone Flute, Oil or Candle, Guarded.... "	7 00
No. 2 Pear, Oil or Candle, Guarded.... "	8 00
No. 3 Pear, Oil or Candle, Guarded.... "	9 00
6 inch Globe, Oil or Candle, Guarded... "	8 00
8 inch Globe, Oil or Candle, Guarded.... "	13 00

A3

SUGAR BOWLS AND COVERS.

Pressed Band Pattern.....per doz.	$3 00
Pressed Fairy Pattern.... "	3 75
Pressed Mitre Diamond Pattern.... "	4 00
Pressed Eugenie Pattern.... "	4 00
Pressed D. and C. Pattern.... "	4 00
Pressed Ray Pattern.... "	4 25
Pressed Crystal.... "	4 00

ALE AND BEER GLASSES.

Pressed Excelsior Ales, or Long Toms.....per doz.	$2 00
Pressed 8 Flute Beer Mugs.... "	2 00
Pressed Argus Ales.... "	1 70
Pressed B. V. Beer Mugs.... "	2 25
Pressed Crystal Beer Mugs.... "	2 00
Pressed Small Pint 6 Flute Ale Tumblers.... "	1 60
Pressed ½ Quart Crystal Ale, Footed.... "	1 60

BITTER BOTTLES.

Pressed 6 Flute.....per doz.	$3 67
Pressed 8 Flute.... "	3 00
Pressed Excelsior.... "	4 33

PRESSED BOWLS.

9 inch Concave Bowls.....per doz.	$8 00
10 inch Excelsior Bowls.... "	9 00
8 inch Mitre Diamond Bowls.... "	6 00
8 inch Mitre Diamond Bowls, with Covers.... "	8 70
10 inch Scollop Diamond Bowls.... "	10 00
8 inch Crystal Bowls.... "	7 00
10 inch Crystal Bowls.... "	11 00
10 inch Leaf Bowls.... "	11 00

SPOON HOLDERS.

Pressed Harp.....per doz.	$2 30
Pressed Crystal.... "	2 50

LANTERNS—Common Mountings.

Cone Flute, Oil or Candle	.........per doz.	$4 33
No. 2 Pear, Oil or Candle	"	4 70
No. 3 Pear, Oil or Candle	"	5 33
Cone Flute, Oil or Candle, Guarded	"	5 33
No. 2 Pear, Oil or Candle, Guarded	"	6 00
No. 3 Pear, Oil or Candle, Guarded	"	6 67

EGG GLASSES.

Pressed Excelsior	.........per doz.	$1 00
Pressed Eugenie	"	1 00
Pressed Crystal	"	1 10

BOWLS FOR HOTELS AND COFFEE HOUSES.

Pressed 8 inch Cracker, Tin Covers	.........per doz.	$12 00
Pressed 10 inch Cracker, Tin Covers	"	16 00

WATER BOTTLES.

Pint Plain	.........per doz.	$3 00
Quart Plain	"	4 00

DECANTERS.

Pressed Pint Excelsior,	and Corks,.........per doz.	$5 00
Pressed Quart Excelsior,	"	6 33
Pressed Pint Rose,	"	5 00
Pressed Quart Gaines,	"	6 33
Pressed Pint Ring Bar,	"	2 75
Pressed Quart Ring Bar,	"	3 75
Pressed Pint Plain Bar,	"	2 50
Pressed Quart Plain Bar,	"	3 00
Pressed Pint R. and R. Pillar,	"	8 00
Pressed Quart R. and R. Pillar,	"	9 33
Pressed Quart Concave Flute,	"	6 33
Cut Quart Concave Flute and Cut Neck,	"	12 00
Pressed Quart Crystal,	"	8 00
Temperance,	.........each,	1 50

PRESSED SAUCERS AND NAPPIES.

3½ inch Star Saucers,	.........per doz. $	40
D. and C. Saucers,	"	3 00
6½ inch Harp Nappies,	"	1 20
6½ inch Harp Nappies and Covers,	"	2 40
6 inch Comet Nappies,	"	1 33
6 inch Comet Nappies and Covers,	"	2 50
7 inch Leaf Nappies,	"	2 00
7 inch Leaf Nappies and Covers,	"	3 33
7 inch Ray Nappies,	"	1 66
6 inch Ray Nappies,	"	1 00
5 inch Ray Nappies,	"	80
4 inch Ray Nappies,	"	50

PRESSED DISHES.

6 inch Shell,	.........per doz. $1	20
7 inch Shell,	"	1 75
8 inch Shell,	"	2 50
7 inch Oval Star,	"	1 65
8 inch Oval Mitre,	"	2 20
Shell Pickle,	"	1 20
7 inch Ray,	"	2 00
9 inch Ray,	"	3 00
Pressed 7 inch Eugenie Dish, on foot,	"	3 00
Pressed 7 inch Eugenie Dish, on foot, and Cover,	"	4 50
Pressed 9 inch Eugenie Dish, on foot,	"	4 50
Pressed 9 inch Eugenie Dish, on foot, and Cover,	"	6 50
Pressed 8 inch Crystal Dish, on foot,	"	4 00
Pressed 8 inch Crystal Dish, on foot, and Cover,	"	5 50

PRESSED SALTS.

Pressed Concave	.........per doz. $	40
Pressed Fillmore	"	1 00
Pressed Mason	"	1 00
Pressed Rope	"	1 33
Pressed Imperial	"	1 33
Pressed Tomato	"	1 60
Pressed Individual	"	65
Pressed Individual, Cut	"	1 75
Pressed Tulip	"	54
Pressed Lotus	"	1 25
Pressed Diamond	"	95

11

LAMP AND GAS GLOBES.

3 inch, Frosted	per doz. $	3 25
4½ inch, Frosted	"	4 70
6 inch, Frosted	"	6 00
Tulip Gas, Frosted	"	4 00
Turban Gas, Frosted	"	4 00
Bell Gas, Frosted	"	4 00
6 inches Cut, Gothic	"	10 00
Tulip Cut, Harp Gas	"	12 00
Tulip Cut, Gothic Gas	"	9 00
6 inches Oregon Cut	"	12 00
Cut Tulip, No. 28	"	10 00
Cut Tulip, No. 27	"	10 00
Cut Tulip, No. 25	"	9 50
Cut Tulip, No. 29	"	10 00
Cut Tulip, No. 31	"	11 00
Cut Tulip, No. 36	"	12 00
Cut Tulip, No. 32	"	11 00
Cut Tulip, Star and Concave	"	9 00
Cut Tulip, No. 52	"	10 00
Cut Turban, No. 39	"	10 00
Cut Turban, No. 38	"	10 00
Cut Turban, No. 53	"	9 00
Cut Bell, No. 41	"	10 00
Cut Bell, No. 42	"	11 00
Cut Bell, No. 44	"	10 00
Cut Bell, No. 43	"	11 00
Cut 6 inch Vine	"	10 00
Cut 4½ inch Vine	"	7 30
Cut 3 inch Vine	"	6 00
Frosted Round Gas	"	4 00
Cut, No. 58	"	7 00
Cut, No. 60, Tulip, Crimped Edge	"	8 00
Frosted Tulip, Crimped Edge	"	4 75
Frosted Fucien, Crimped Edge	"	4 50
Cut, No. 61, Fucien, Crimped Edge	"	6 00

10

GOBLETS.

Pressed Excelsior	per doz. $	1 90
Pressed Band	"	1 80
Pressed Charleston	"	1 90
Pressed 6 Flute	"	1 75
Pressed H. S	"	2 00
Pressed Diamond	"	2 33
Pressed Eugenie	"	2 00
Pressed Crystal	"	2 00
Pressed Mioton Hotel	"	2 00
Pressed Argus	"	2 00

WINE GLASSES.

Pressed 6 Flute	per doz. $	95
Pressed Ashburton	"	95
Pressed Excelsior	"	1 00
Pressed H. S	"	1 10
Pressed Diamond	"	1 25
Pressed Eugenie	"	1 10
Pressed Crystal	"	1 10
Pressed Mioton Hotel	"	1 00
Pressed Argus	"	1 00

LIQUORS AND CORDIALS.

Pressed Charleston	per doz. $	95
Pressed Eugenie	"	1 00
Pressed Mioton Hotel	"	1 00

LAMP CHIMNEYS.

2 inch, 2⅛ 2¼, 2⅜ and 2½ inch Solar	per doz. $	1 00
2 inch Camphene	"	1 75
2¾ inch and 3 inch Camphene	"	2 00
3¼ inch and 3½ inch Camphene	"	2 25
3½ inch Turn-over Globes	"	4 00
1½ inch Deitz Chimneys, or Coal Oil	"	1 20
2¾ inch Deitz Chimneys, or Coal Oil	"	1 50

APOTHECARIES' SHOP FURNITURE.

MADE OF FLINT GLASS.

Specie Jars, with Tin Japanned Covers.

3 gallon.............	per doz. $10 00	½ gallon.............	per doz. $2 40
2 gallon.............	" 6 00	1 quart.............	" 1 75
6 quart.............	" 5 00	1 pint.............	" 1 12¼
1 gallon.............	" 3 60	½ pint.............	" 80
3 quart.............	" 3 00		

Specie Jars, with Tin Japanned Covers.

SQUAT SHAPE.

2 gallon.............	per doz. $6 25	1 quart.............	per doz. $1 80
1 gallon.............	3 75	1 pint.............	1 20
3 quart.............	3 12¼	½ pint.............	90
½ gallon.............	2 50		

Two Ring Jars, with Glass Covers.

2 gallon.............	per doz. $15 00	3 quart.............	per doz. $7 00
6 quart.............	10 00	½ gallon.............	6 00
1 gallon.............	9 00	1 quart.............	4 00

Confectionery Jars made to order.
Large Show Jars made to order.

Tinctures, with Ground Crown Stoppers.

2 gallon.............	per doz. $7 25	1 quart.............	per doz. $2 00
6 quart.............	5 50	1 pint.............	1 25
1 gallon.............	4 25	½ pint and 4 oz.......	1 00
½ gallon.............	3 00	1 and 2 oz.......	80

LAMPS.

Pressed Harp Hand, for Oil,...............	per doz.	$2 00
Pressed Harp Hand, for Fluid,.............	"	2 64
Pressed Plain Hand, for Oil,..............	"	2 10
Pressed Plain Hand, for Fluid,............	"	2 75
Pressed Leaf, for Oil,...................	"	3 33
Pressed Leaf, for Fluid,..................	"	4 00
Pressed L. and C., for Oil,...............	"	4 00
Pressed L. and C., for Fluid,.............	"	4 66
Pressed Eugenie, for Oil,.................	"	5 33
Pressed Eugenie, for Fluid,...............	"	6 00
Pressed Night, for Oil,...................	"	1 33
Pressed Night, for Fluid,.................	"	1 65
Pressed Gaines, for Oil,..................	"	6 67
Pressed Gaines, for Fluid,................	"	6 00
Pressed Star, for Oil,....................	"	6 00
Pressed Star, for Fluid,..................	"	5 33
Pressed Turnip Stand, Coal Oil...........	"	8 00
Pressed Turnip Peg, for Oil,..............	"	1 50
Pressed Turnip Peg, for Fluid,............	"	2 00
Pressed Turnip Stand, or Kitchen, for Fluid,......	"	4 50
Pressed Turnip Stand, or Kitchen, for Oil,......	"	3 75

SUNDRIES.

Pressed Toys..........................	per gross,	$2 70
Pressed Bird Fountains.................	per doz.	1 65
Pressed Seed Boxes....................	"	1 33
Pressed 1 inch Rose Knobs and Pins.....	"	75
Pressed 2 inch Rose Knobs and Pins.....	"	1 00
Julep Tubes..........................	"	20
Fish Globes made to order......each, from 50 cents up to		5 00
Shoemakers' Globes....................	per doz.	3 00
Bird Baths...........................	"	1 00
Butter Prints........................	"	2 00
White Enamel Glass Eggs...............	"	75

14

Salt Mouths, with Ground Crown Stoppers.

2 gallon..............	per doz. $8 50		1 quart..............	per doz.	$2 25
6 quart..............	" 6 50		1 pint..............	"	1 50
1 gallon..............	" 5 25		½ pint..............	"	1 25
½ gallon..............	" 3 50		1, 2 and 4 oz.........	"	1 00

Syringes.

Pocket Penis..............	per doz.	$1 25
1 oz. Male, Capped..............	"	1 75
2 oz. Male, Capped..............	"	2 25
3 oz. Male, Capped..............	"	2 75
1 oz. Female, Capped..............	"	2 25
2 oz. Female, Capped..............	"	2 75
3 oz. Female, Capped..............	"	3 25
4 oz. Female, Capped..............	"	4 00
Curved Womb..............	"	5 00
Straight Womb..............	"	4 50
Ear..............	"	3 50
Eye..............	"	2 50

Graduates.

Minimum..............	per doz.	$4 20
1 oz..............	"	3 60
2 oz..............	"	4 20
3 oz..............	"	4 80
4 oz..............	"	5 40
6 oz..............	"	6 00
8 oz..............	"	7 20
12 oz..............	"	9 00
16 oz..............	"	12 00
32 oz..............	"	21 00

Show Globes.

½ gallon, 2 pieces, cone or globe shape..............	each $	50
1 gallon, 2 pieces, cone or globe shape..............	"	75
2 gallon, 2 pieces, cone or globe shape..............	"	1 25
3 gallon, 3 pieces, cone or globe shape..............	"	2 50
1 gallon, 3 pieces, pear shape..............	"	1 25
2 gallon, 3 pieces, pear shape..............	"	1 75
3 gallon, 3 pieces, pear shape..............	"	2 50
5 gallon, 4 pieces, French style..............	"	6 00
5 gallon, 3 pieces, French style, engraved, net..............	"	12 00
3 gallon, 3 pieces, French style..............	"	5 00

15

Mortars and Pestles.

Gill..............	per doz.	$6 00
½ Pint..............	"	6 00
Pint..............	"	9 00
Quart..............	"	15 00

Funnels.

Gill..............	per doz. $	75
½ Pint..............	"	90
Pint..............	"	1 00
Quart..............	"	1 25
½ Gallon..............	"	1 75
Assorted..............	"	1 25

Miscellaneous.

Breast Pipes..............	per doz. $2 00		Nipple Shields..............	per doz.	$2 00
Nipple Shells..............	" 60		Flat Pessaries..............	"	1 25
Nursing Bottles..............	2 00		Globe Pessaries..............	"	2 00
½, 1 and 2 oz. Cupping Glasses..............	"	60			
Nested Cupping Glasses..............	"	1 00			
4 oz. Cupping Glasses..............	"	1 00			
8 oz. Cupping Glasses..............	"	1 25			
Glass Speculums..............	"	3 25			
Male and Female Urinals..............	"	3 75			
¼, ½, 1 and 2 drachm Flint Vials..............	per gro.	2 00			
1 and 2 oz. Heavy Flint Vials, for Saddle Bags..............		3 50			
Glass Inhalers..............	per doz.	3 75			
Glass Spittoons..............	"	2 50			
Vaccine Glasses..............	"	3 75			
Eye Glasses..............	"	2 00			
Proof Vials..............	"	1 00			

☞ Glass Tubing, Cane, Spirit Lamps, Electrical Cylinders, Retorts, Receivers, Florence Flasks, together with Chemical and Philosophical Apparatus, all made to order.

☞ Window Glass, Vials, Bottles and Flasks furnished on the most reasonable terms.

16

TERMS

◆

All Bills under $100, Cash.

All Bills over $100, 4 months.

All Bills over $500, 6 months.

Less   per cent. discount.

☞ With the latest improvements, and superior facilities for manufacturing, we can assure our customers that there is nothing elegant or extra in Flint Glass Ware, made or furnished in this vicinity, but we make and supply.

☞ No care or expense is spared to furnish the LATEST AND BEST STYLES of Pressed and other Wares to be had in the United States.

☞ Our facilities are unsurpassed for making every variety of APOTHECARIES' SHOP FURNITURE, of the best quality, and supplying it in large quantities at short notice. The attention of Wholesale Druggists invited.

☞ To Dealers who buy large lots, and wish uniformly good merchantable ware, packed in good order, we think we can offer such advantages, in quality and reasonable prices, as will repay their attention.

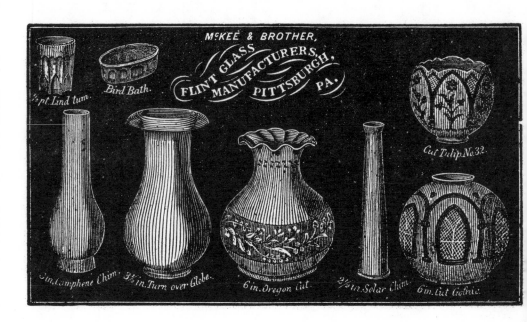

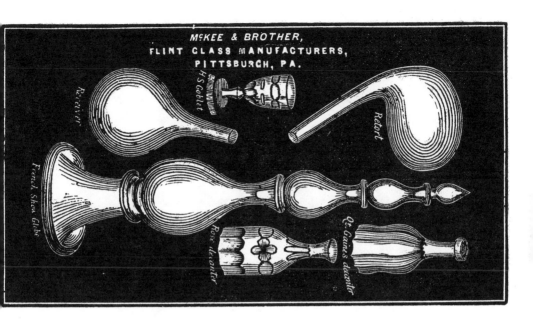

McKEE & BROTHER,
FLINT GLASS MANUFACTURERS, PITTSBURGH, PA.

7 in. Star dish. Ex Goblet. Ex Egg. 3 in. Dia.d Cup plate. Quart Ex Pitcher. Pint 6 Flute tum.

Ex Ale.

iury Sugar & Cov. 8 in. Mitre Dish. 14 Can Tin. French Candlestick.

McKEE & BROTHER,
FLINT GLASS MANUFACTURERS, PITTSBURGH, PA.

Tulip Cut Gothic. Ex. Can Brit.

7½ in. Leaf Sweetmeat & Cov. 9 in. D. & C. Saucer. 9 in. Ray Dish.

Bend Goblet. 7 in. Ray Nappie. Cut Turban No. 5¾. 7 in. Ray Dish. ½ qt. Band footed tum.

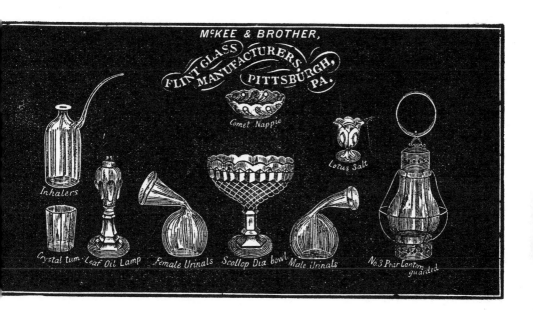

McKEE & BROTHER,

FLINT GLASS MANUFACTURERS, PITTSBURGH, PA.

Comet Nappie

Inhalers

Lotus Salt

Crystal tum. Leaf Oil Lamp   Female Urinals   Scollop Dia bowl   Male Urinals   No.3 Pear Lantern guarded

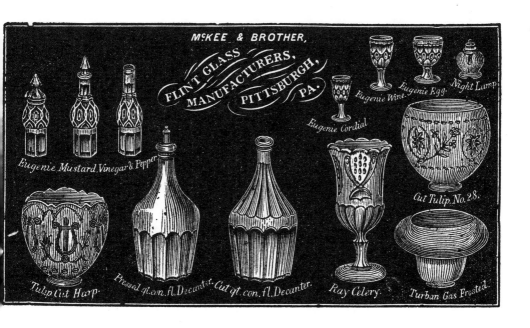

McKEE & BROTHER,

FLINT GLASS MANUFACTURERS, PITTSBURGH, PA.

Eugenie Wine.   Eugenie Egg.   Night Lamp.

Eugenie Cordial

Eugenie Mustard, Vinegar & Pepper.

Cut Tulip. No. 28.

Tulip Cut Harp.   Pressed qt. con. fl. Decanter. Cut qt. con. fl. Decanter.   Ray Celery.   Turban Gas Frosted.

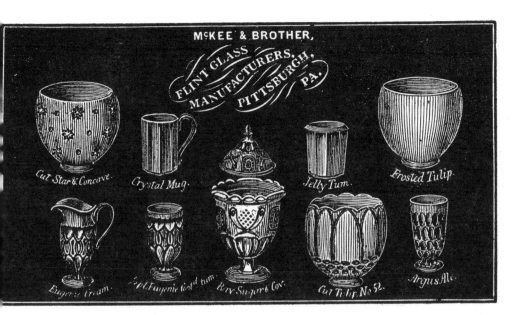

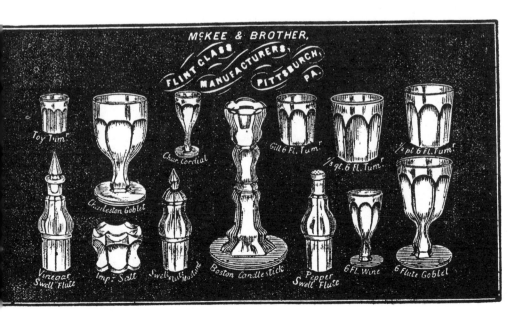

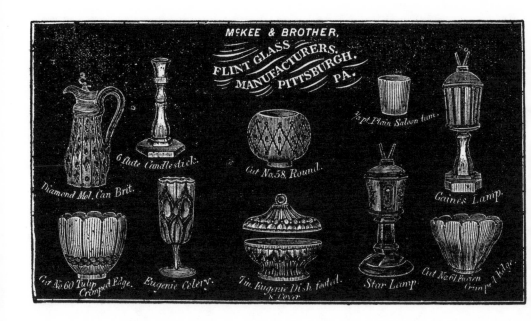

McKEE & BROTHER,
FLINT GLASS MANUFACTURERS, PITTSBURGH, PA.

Qt. R.& R. Pillared Decanter.   Cut Bell, No. 44.   Cut Bell, No. 42.   Eugenie Lamp

Cut Tulip No. 29.   Cut Tulip No. 27.   Eugenie Sugar & Cov.   Cut Tulip No. 36.   Cut Tulip No. 31.

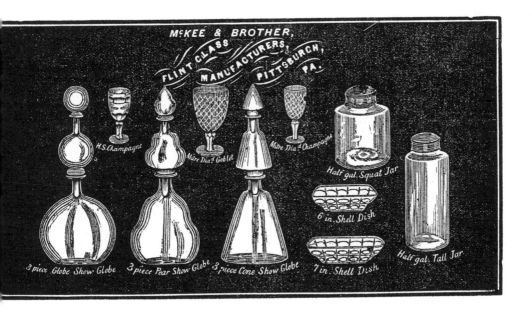

McKEE & BROTHER,
FLINT GLASS MANUFACTURERS, PITTSBURGH, PA.

H.S.Champagne.   Mitre Dia.d Goblet.   Mitre Dia.d Champagne.   Half gal. Squat Jar

6 in. Shell Dish

3 piece Globe Show Globe   3 piece Pear Show Globe   3 piece Cone Show Globe   7 in. Shell Dish   Half gal. Tall Jar

THE 1864 CATALOG

A sharp difference exists between the type of material advertised in 1864 and that in 1860. The 1864 catalog records the expected changes in style and the strong emphasis on pattern glass tableware. Many of the sundries and globes had been dropped.

New patterns like Brilliant (13 pieces), Prism (18), Stedman (19), Sprig (26), and Ribbed Leaf (Bellflower, 42) offer convincing proof of the change. Less important newcomers also emphasize this: Ring, Vine, Mirror and New York. Ring is reminiscent of a blown Sandwich pattern of the same name. Vine, of course, is like Bellflower but with a simpler design; New York is the ubiquitous Honeycomb with the smallest row of combs.

When a pattern was presented in 1864, there were different forms and not merely different sizes. For instance, Sprig, the first pattern which the M'Kees patented, is shown in 14 forms out of 26 pieces. Three standby patterns in 1860 continued in 1864: Eugenie (13), Excelsior (15), and Crystal (20). Clearly the industry had entered the period of large sets.

Crystal poses a question of nomenclature that confronts both collectors and students. In a James B. Lyon catalog, 1861, Crystal is pictured in three different designs: lines within a loop, lines crossed within a loop, and large bowls with diamonds around the bottom of the bowl, clear loops rising to the rim.[11] This last is not too different from M'Kee Scalloped Diamond. When M'Kee pictures 20 pieces of Crystal in 1864, his pattern is plain—very like Huber. Two large bowls, however, have elongated Diamond panels at the base of the bowls—the same idea which Lyon employed.

Another perennial question troubling students is the dating of patterns. Most students of American glass in the 1950s were much too generous in assigning early dates for pressed glass.

Collectors of Bellflower have been somewhat united in declaring

[11] Innes, *op. cit.*, Fig. 372.

it to be a Sandwich pattern, and are apt to think in terms of the early 1850s. Documentation for this opinion has not yet been offered. We know that manufacturers quickly copied popular patterns that had not been patented. Nevertheless it is difficult to believe that M'Kee was focusing most of his 1864 advertising on a Sandwich pattern that had been produced ten years before. He illustrated 28 different shapes out of 42 shown. Objectively, the undocumented attribution is possible but questionable; no other pressed pattern has had so many undocumented statements made about it.

The introduction of the soda-lime formula does not help solve the problem because many pieces are found in soda-lime as well as in lead. The variety found within the pattern is itself confusing: single vine or double vine; coarse ribbing or fine ribbing; scalloped rims or plain; pontil mark present or absent; lead or soda-lime glass.

The only documentation is the M'Kee 1864 catalog with 42 pieces pictured. Most of the attributions to M'Kee and Brothers had come from the few pieces in the 1868 catalog partly published by Ruth Webb Lee and A. C. Revi, and Charles Messer Stow's warning article in the October 1929 *Antiquarian*, "Sandwich Glass that Pittsburgh Made."

Ruth Webb Lee had access to the 1868 M'Kee & Brothers catalog which pictures seven pieces of Bellflower. In spite of this fact, she assigned Bellflower to the 1840s because, as she said, she found more pieces in Bellflower handled by the pontil rod. However, she does not credit M'Kee with having made the pattern. The Sandwich claim seems to rest on the fragments found by Francis Wynn and the five differences he perceived in the forms. Support for the claim has also been offered by Frank W. Chipman,[12] but we have no actual documentation. Again and again glass scholars talk of other factories producing Bellflower. One factory mentioned that can be disproved is that of J. B. Lyon of Pittsburgh. In the three Lyon catalogs that exist (1861 dated, ca. 1876, and ca. 1884) no picture of Bellflower appears nor is any reference made to it. The late James Rose, an early student of Midwestern glass, said "If you can prove any piece of Bellflower was made before 1860, I'll grind it up and eat it!"[13]

The final judgment on Bellflower must be formed by the individual scholar. Without contradiction, Bellflower was the leading pattern pictured in the M'Kee & Brothers catalog for 1864. We know of no other pressed pattern pictured as early in as many pieces. Undoubt-

---

[12] Chipman, Frank W. *The Romance of Old Sandwich Glass*, Sandwich Publishing Co., Inc., 1932, p. 85.
[13] Private communication to Lowell Innes.

edly, large sets of pressed tableware were now salable items.

The 1864 changes in style fit into several categories. Sprig and Ribbed Leaf (Bellflower) are reeded with stylized figures. Stedman, Tulip, and Ribbed follow the artistic principle of reeding, but their designs are smoother and rounder than thin reeds. Brilliant continues the spirit of cut glass in using geometric figures. Gaines, Crystal, Flute, and Mioton are in the paneled group. Prism may seem to fit with reeding, yet often the lines are elongated panels.

Molasses or syrup cans, popular in both catalogs, were mold-blown in the Diamond and Oval pattern, in the Rose, and in No. 14, six panels alternating, a large star in one and two circles in the next. Of course, a free-blown undecorated syrup was always available.

Often the term Ribbed belongs to pressed glass as does Ring, usually in relation to lamps. Where the catalog adds Fine Ribbed it is safe to identify the technique as pattern-molding in decanters and cruets. It is fairly certain that Pillared means pillar-molding, usually applied to decanters and cruets. Judgments should be governed by the pictures, however, when a handsome quart pitcher obviously pillar-molded is described as Ribbed.

In lighting, the picture had completely changed since 1860. The process of refining kerosene had been perfected in 1859, and in 1860 it was apparently just coming into use as a lamp fuel. In the 1864 catalog, there were 27 kerosene lamps of various types shown, all without chimneys (which could be purchased separately). Kerosene gave a poor light without a chimney. The variations available and the Price List raised this total to 33 patterns, some available without burners, plus 17 peg lamps in large and small sizes. There were five lanterns which were still available with candles as well as with kerosene. One footed lamp and a small night lamp were available with burning-fluid wicks. Only the Gaines and Turnip lamps were held over from the 1860 catalog unchanged except for the substitution of kerosene burners for those using burning fluid. Two suspension lamps to hang from metal brackets (a new style) are shown in the catalog, and wall brackets with reflectors and a harp hanger are available separately. One 3-1/2" lamp base which appears to have a brass stem and a square black or white glass base is also shown, and the Price List indicates it could also be had in 4" and 5" sizes.

The sale of separate fonts and bases indicates that retailers often combined them as local sales dictated. Packing and shipping were also easier with separate fonts and bases, and replacements could be supplied locally with no trouble. Most lamps were put together with a metal collar and some sort of plaster. It was possible for the retailer to put M'Kee bases on fonts from some other firm if customer demand warranted it. It was not until after 1876 when Atterbury patented his one-piece "BOSS" lamp that the use of the metal collars nearly disappeared.

There are two hand lamps, one vertically ribbed and the other horizontally ribbed. Most of the lamps in 1864 had one-piece glass stems and bases; only five are shown with brass stems and colored bases, in addition to the separate brass stem mentioned above. A separate undated Price List of about 1863 lists 67 carbon-oil or kerosene lamps and none for whale oil or burning fluid. The Price List also offers nine lamp chimneys, including those for solar lamps, camphene, and coal oil. The Bacon's burners (for burning without a chimney) were still available in 1864.

The blown, cut, and engraved lampshades of the earlier catalog had completely disappeared just four years later. Their place was taken by the chimney, which was to become an important branch of the glass business in Pittsburgh. It is truly amazing to see how speedily kerosene replaced all other lamp fuels.

Most of the lamps pictured were available in two styles, with a tall glass stem and foot or with a brass collar and glass base. Patterns pictured in the catalog are: Argus, Concave, Gaines, Prism, Ribbed, Ring, RL, Shell, Sprig, Stedman, Tulip, Turnip, and Vine.

The six-flute candlesticks have been dropped from the 1864 catalog, leaving only three styles of candlesticks. This is more likely to indicate that the plain six-flute candlestick was going out of style than that candlesticks themselves were used less.

In the remaining sections of the catalog—those listing salts, household sundries and druggists' wares—there is scarcely a change from the 1860 catalog. The same patterns of salts are available and the same household sundries and toys.

Although collectors are more interested in tableware, this part of the catalogs is useful for the documentation of druggists' show globes, ring jars, and other blown wares which continued to be manufactured with little stylistic change through the second half of the nineteenth century.

PICTURED IN THE 1864 CATALOG

PATTERN	NUMBER OF PIECES	PATTERN	NUMBER OF PIECES
Argus—3 Type 1		Boston candlestick	1
—3 Type 2	6	Brilliant	13
Band	3	B.V.*	1
Bigler	2	Charleston*	3

PATTERN	NUMBER OF PIECES	PATTERN	NUMBER OF PIECES
Comet	2	New York	5
Concave	4	Number 14/mol. can.	1
Crystal	20	Number 17	3
Diamond	3	Oval Mitre	1
Diamond/m.o.	1	Oval Star	1
Diamond, Scalloped	1	Pillared	6
Dolphin candlestick	1	Plain	2
Eugenie	13	Prism	18
Excelsior	15	Ray	9
Fairy	1	Ribbed	4
Fillmore	1	Ribbed Leaf (Bellflower)	42
Fine Ribbed	1	Ring	2
Finger Flute*	3	Rope	1
Flute	24	Rose	2
Flute, Swelled	3	Shell	7
French candlestick	1	Sprig	26
Gaines	4	Star	1
Gauche	3	Stedman	19
Imperial	1	Temperance*	1
Leaf (Loop)	3	Tomato	1
Lotus	1	Tulip	5
Mason	1	Turnip	2
Mioton	5	Vine	2
Mirror	4		
Mudge*	1		

* Tumbler or mug design.

Frederick McKee

PRICES

OF

GLASS WARE

MANUFACTURED BY

M'KEE & BROTHERS,

No. 17 Wood Street, Corner First and Wood Sts.

PITTSBURGH, PA.

ENGRAVINGS BY J. G. SEYMOUR.

PITTSBURGH:
PRINTED BY W. S. HAVEN, CORNER OF WOOD AND THIRD STREETS.

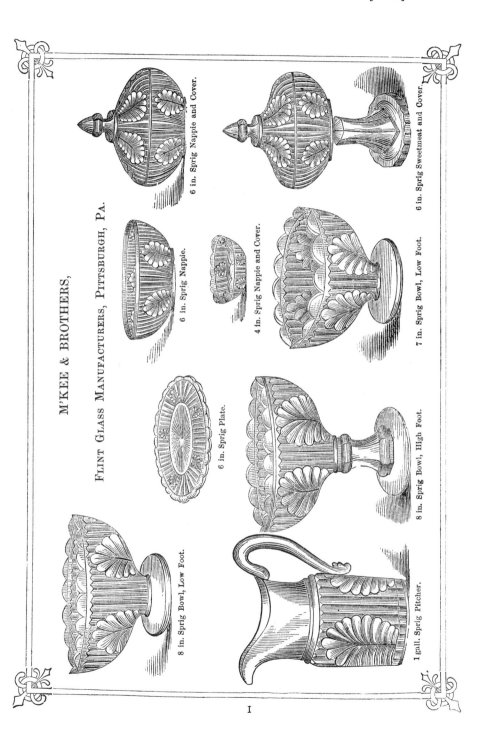

M'KEE & BROTHERS,

FLINT GLASS MANUFACTURERS, PITTSBURGH, PA.

6 in. Sprig Nappie and Cover.

6 in. Sprig Sweetmeat and Cover.

6 in. Sprig Nappie.

4 in. Sprig Nappie and Cover.

7 in. Sprig Bowl, Low Foot.

6 in. Sprig Plate.

8 in. Sprig Bowl, High Foot.

8 in. Sprig Bowl, Low Foot.

1 gall. Sprig Pitcher.

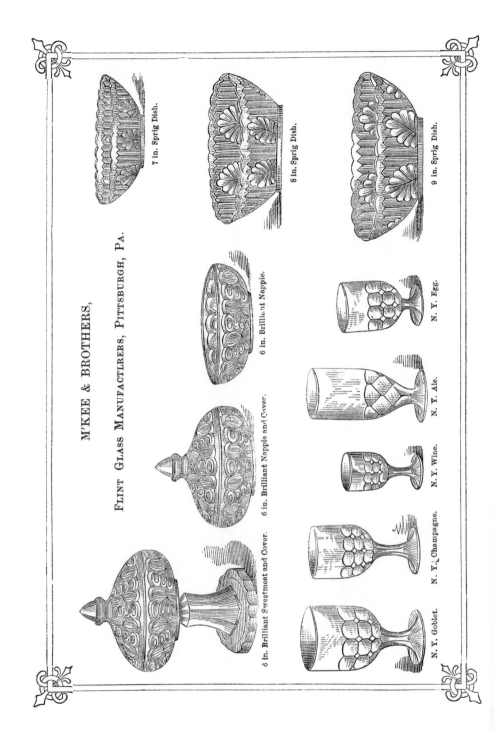

M'KEE & BROTHERS,

FLINT GLASS MANUFACTLRERS, PITTSBURGH, PA.

7 in. Sprig Dish.

8 in. Sprig Dish.

9 in. Sprig Dish.

6 in. Brilliant Nappie.

6 in. Brilliant Nappie and Cover.

6 in. Brilliant Sweetmeat and Cover.

6 in. Brilliant Sweetmeat and Cover.

N. Y. Egg.

N. Y. Ale.

N. Y. Wine.

N. Y. Champagne.

N. Y. Goblet.

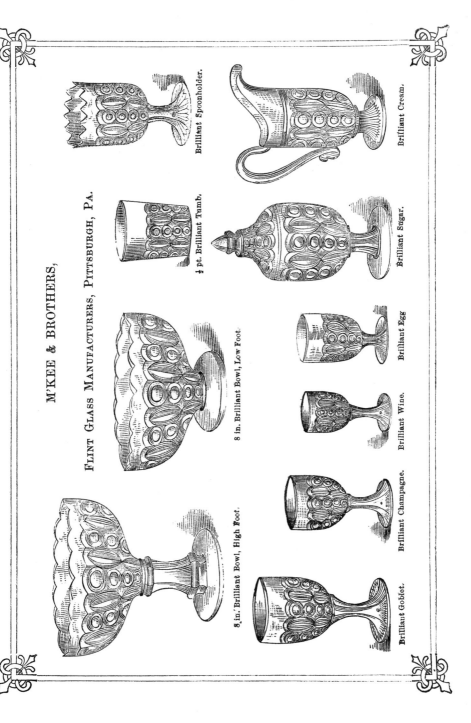

M'KEE & BROTHERS,

FLINT GLASS MANUFACTURERS, PITTSBURGH, PA.

Brilliant Spoonholder.

Brilliant Cream.

½ pt. Brilliant Tumb.

Brilliant Sugar.

8 in. Brilliant Bowl, Low Foot.

Brilliant Egg.

Brilliant Wine.

8 in. Brilliant Bowl, High Foot.

Brilliant Champagne.

Brilliant Goblet.

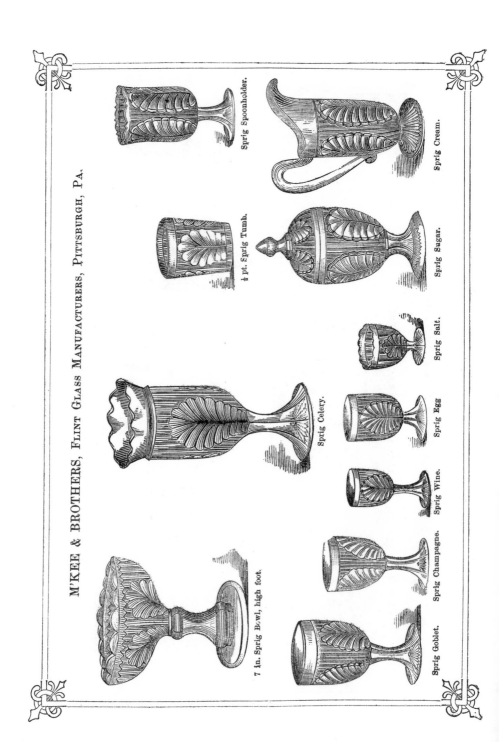

M'KEE & BROTHERS, FLINT GLASS MANUFACTURERS, PITTSBURGH, PA.

Sprig Spoonholder.

Sprig Cream.

½ pt. Sprig Tumb.

Sprig Sugar.

Sprig Salt.

Sprig Celery.

Sprig Egg

Sprig Wine.

Sprig Champagne.

7 in. Sprig Bowl, high foot.

Sprig Goblet.

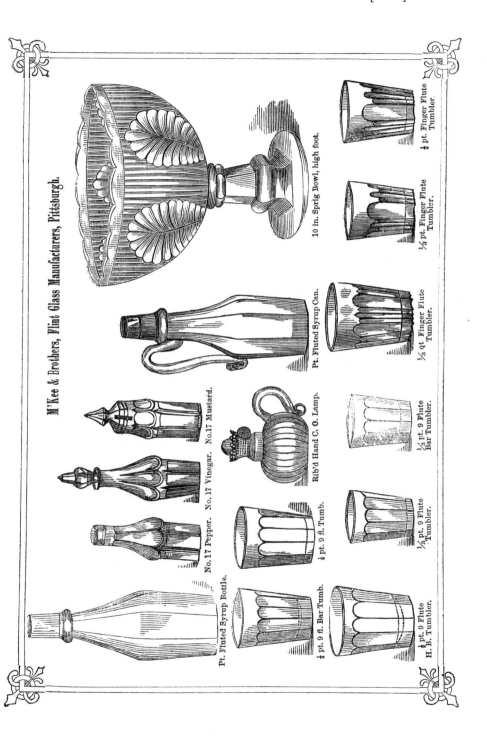

M'Kee & Brothers, Flint Glass Manufacturers, Pittsburgh.

10 in. Sprig Bowl, high foot.

Pt. Fluted Syrup Can.

No.17 Mustard.

No.17 Vinegar.

Rib'd Hand C. O. Lamp.

No.17 Pepper.

Pt. Fluted Syrup Bottle.

¼ pt. 9 fl. Tumb.

¼ pt. 9 fl. Bar Tumb.

¼ pt. Finger Flute Tumbler.

⅓ pt. Finger Flute Tumbler.

⅓ qt Finger Flute Tumbler.

½ pt. 9 Flute Bar Tumbler.

½ pt. 9 Flute Tumbler.

¼ pt. 9 Flute H. B. Tumbler.

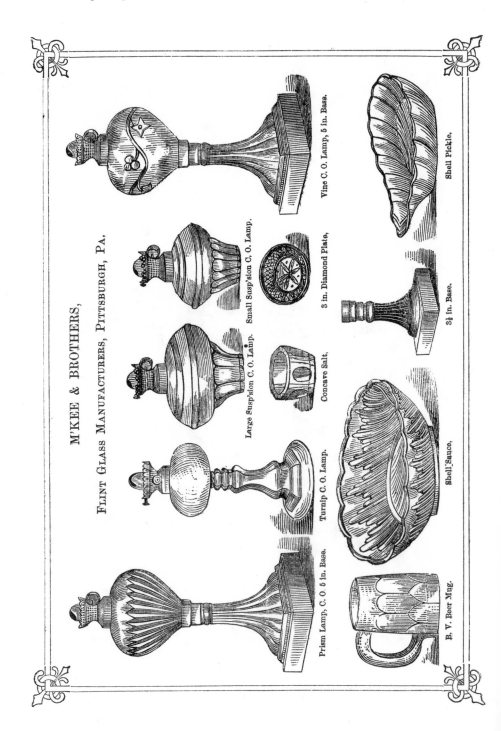

M'KEE & BROTHERS,

FLINT GLASS MANUFACTURERS, PITTSBURGH, PA.

Vine C. O. Lamp, 5 in. Base.

Shell Pickle.

Small Susp'sion C. O. Lamp.

3 in. Diamond Plate.

3¼ in. Base.

Large Susp'sion C. O. Lamp.

Concave Salt.

Turnip C. O. Lamp.

Shell Sauce.

Prism Lamp, C. O. 5 in. Base.

B. V. Beer Mug.

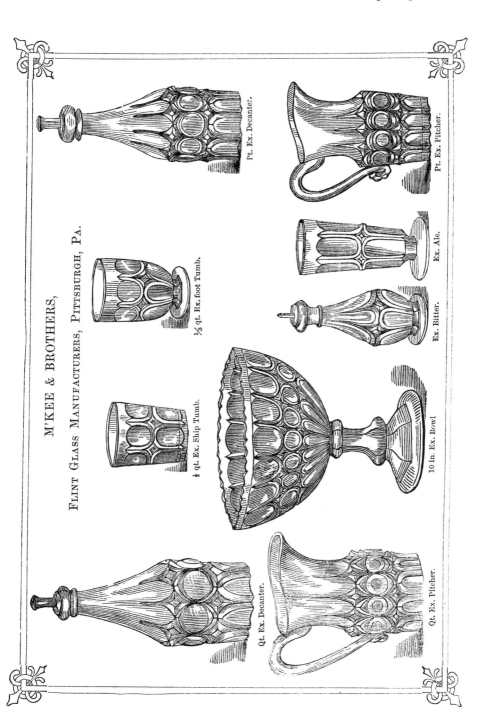

M'KEE & BROTHERS,

FLINT GLASS MANUFACTURERS, PITTSBURGH, PA.

Pt. Ex. Decanter.

Pt. Ex. Pitcher.

Ex. Ale.

Ex. Bitter.

1/3 qt. Ex. foot Tumb.

1/2 qt. Ex. Ship Tumb.

10 in. Ex. Bowl

Qt. Ex. Decanter.

Qt. Ex. Pitcher.

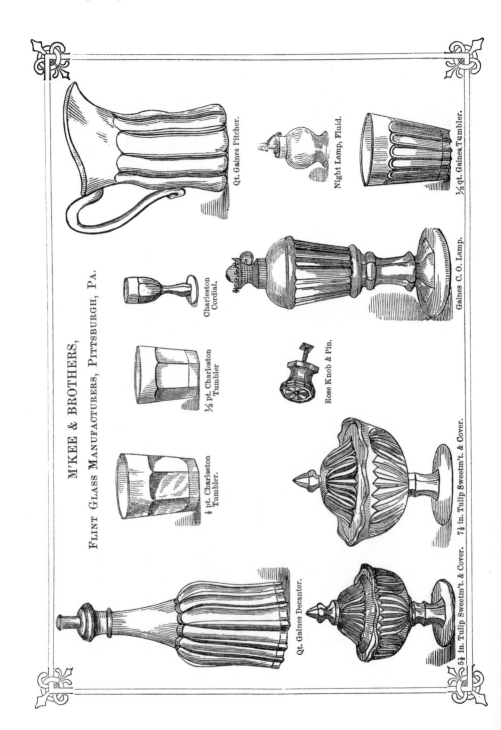

M'KEE & BROTHERS,
FLINT GLASS MANUFACTURERS, PITTSBURGH, PA.

Qt. Gaines Pitcher.

Night Lamp, Fluid.

⅓ qt. Gaines Tumbler.

Charleston Cordial.

Gaines C. O. Lamp.

½ pt. Charleston Tumbler

Rose Knob & Pin.

¼ pt. Charleston Tumbler.

7½ in. Tulip Sweetm't. & Cover.

Qt. Gaines Decanter.

5¼ in. Tulip Sweetm't. & Cover.

McKEE & BROTHERS,

Flint Glass Manufacturers, Pittsburgh, Pa.

¼ gall. Ring Jar.

Saloon Pepper.

½ gall. Tincture.

6 Flute Bitter.

Band Goblet.

Pint Plain Syrup Can.

⅓ qt. Band, foot Tumbler.

Rose Mo. Can, Brit. Top.

Band Sugar.

Diamond Mo. Can, Brit. Top.

½ gall. Saltmouth.

No. 14 Mo. Can, Brit. Top.

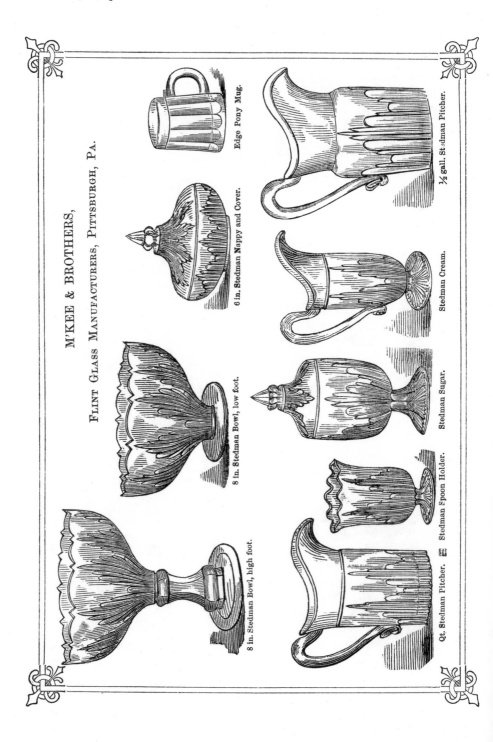

M'KEE & BROTHERS,

FLINT GLASS MANUFACTURERS, PITTSBURGH, PA.

Edge Pony Mug.

6 in. Stedman Nappy and Cover.

8 in. Stedman Bowl, low foot.

8 in. Stedman Bowl, high foot.

½ gall. Stedman Pitcher.

Stedman Cream.

Stedman Sugar.

Stedman Spoon Holder.

Qt. Stedman Pitcher.

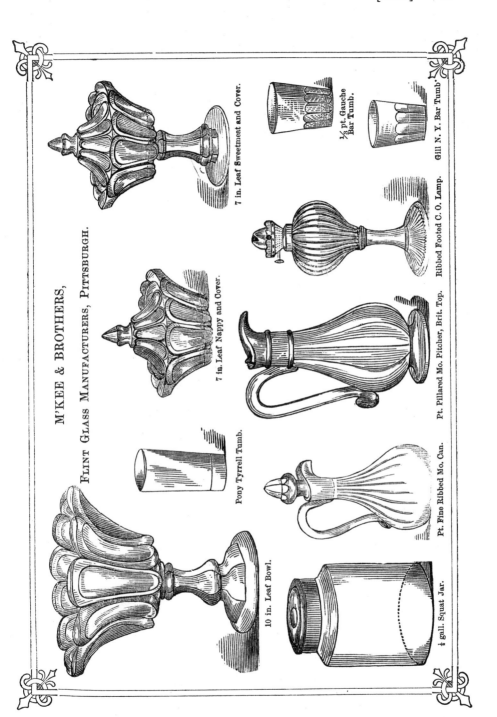

M'KEE & BROTHERS,
FLINT GLASS MANUFACTURERS, PITTSBURGH.

7 in. Leaf Sweetmeat and Cover.

⅓ pt. Gauche Bar Tumb.

Gill N. Y. Bar Tumb.

Ribbed Footed C. O. Lamp.

7 in. Leaf Nappy and Cover.

Pt. Pillared Mo. Pitcher, Brit. Top.

Pony Tyrrell Tumb.

Pt. Fine Ribbed Mo. Can.

10 in. Leaf Bowl.

¼ gall. Squat Jar.

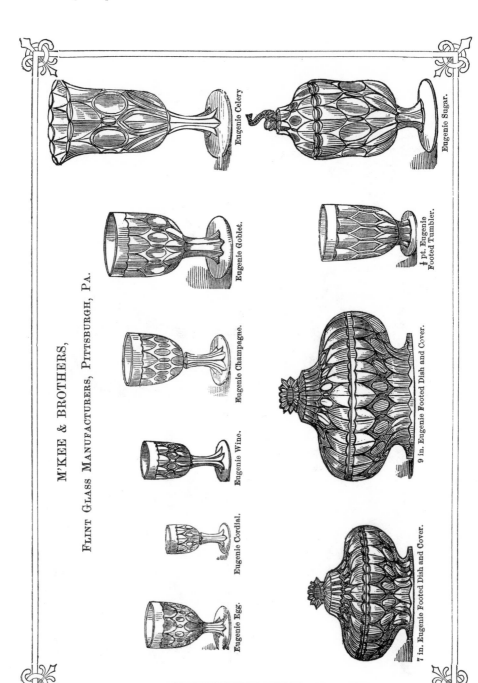

M'KEE & BROTHERS,

FLINT GLASS MANUFACTURERS, PITTSBURGH, PA.

Eugenie Celery.

Eugenie Sugar.

Eugenie Goblet.

½ pt. Eugenie Footed Tumbler.

Eugenie Champagne.

9 in. Eugenie Footed Dish and Cover.

Eugenie Wine.

Eugenie Cordial.

Eugenie Egg.

7 in. Eugenie Footed Dish and Cover.

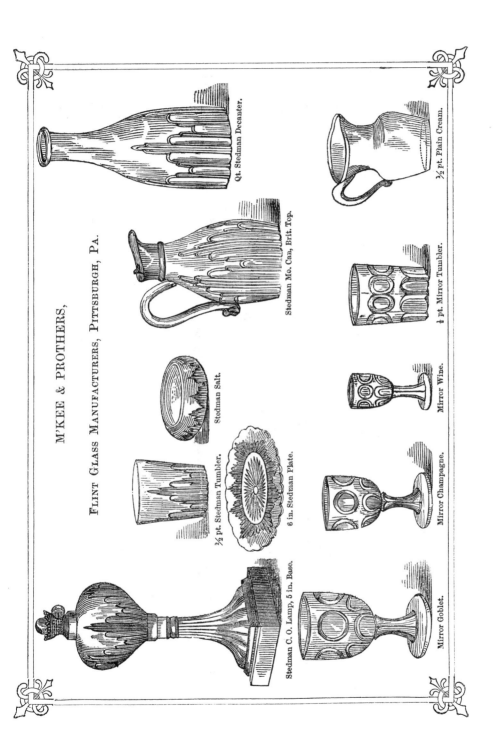

M'KEE & PROTHERS,

FLINT GLASS MANUFACTURERS, PITTSBURGH, PA.

Qt. Stedman Decanter.

½ pt. Plain Cream.

Stedman Mo. Can, Brit. Top.

¼ pt. Mirror Tumbler.

Stedman Salt.

Mirror Wine.

½ pt. Stedman Tumbler.

6 in. Stedman Plate.

Mirror Champagne.

Stedman C. O. Lamp, 5 in. Base.

Mirror Goblet.

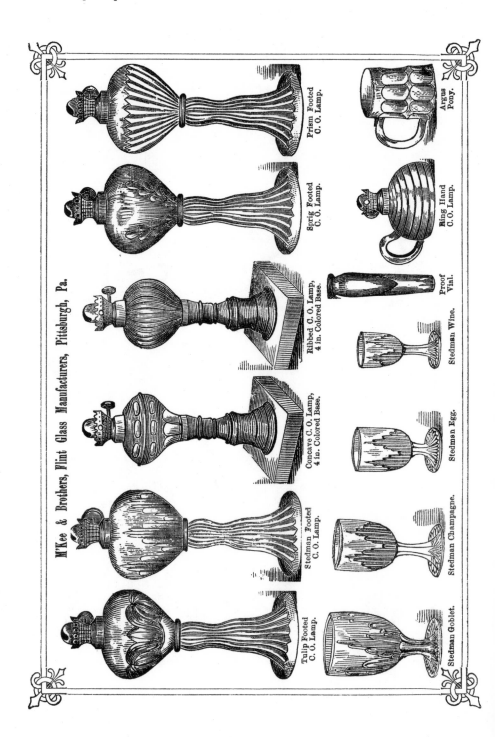

M'Kee & Brothers, Flint Glass Manufacturers, Pittsburgh, Pa.

Prism Footed C. O. Lamp.

Sprig Footed C. O. Lamp.

Ribbed C. O. Lamp, 4 in. Colored Base.

Concave C. O. Lamp, 4 in. Colored Base.

Stedman Footed C. O. Lamp.

Tulip Footed C. O. Lamp.

Argus Pony.

Ring Hand C. O. Lamp.

Proof Vial.

Stedman Wine.

Stedman Egg.

Stedman Champagne.

Stedman Goblet.

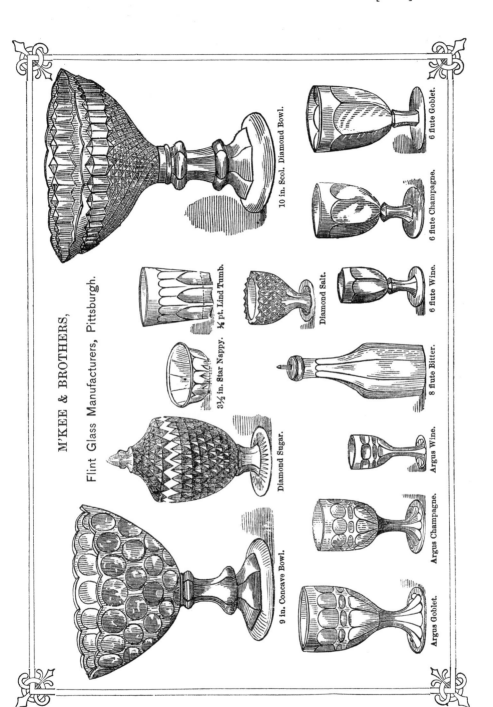

M'KEE & BROTHERS,

Flint Glass Manufacturers, Pittsburgh.

10 in. Scol. Diamond Bowl.

6 flute Goblet.

6 flute Champagne.

6 flute Wine.

¼ pt. Lind Tumb.

3½ in. Star Nappy.

Diamond Salt.

8 flute Bitter.

Diamond Sugar.

Argus Wine.

Argus Champagne.

9 in. Concave Bowl.

Argus Goblet.

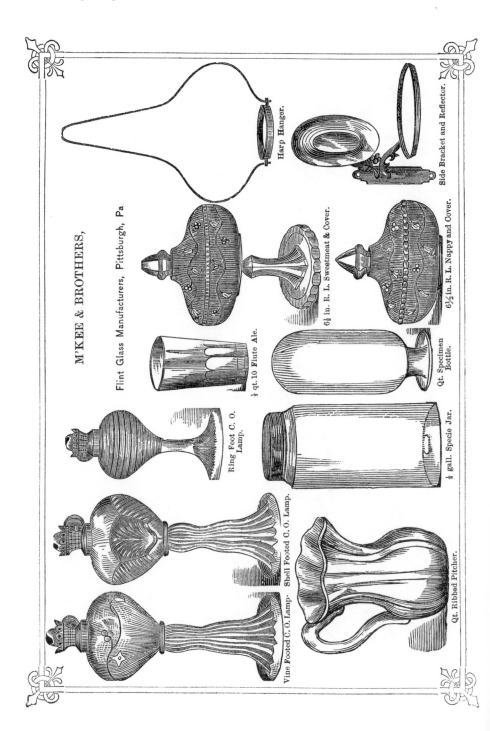

M'KEE & BROTHERS,

Flint Glass Manufacturers, Pittsburgh, Pa

Harp Hanger.

Side Bracket and Reflector.

6¼ in. R. L. Sweetmeat & Cover.

6½ in. R. L. Nappy and Cover.

½ qt. 10 Flute Ale.

Qt. Specimen Bottle.

Ring Foot C. O. Lamp.

½ gall. Specie Jar.

Shell Footed C. O. Lamp.

Vine Footed C. O. Lamp.

Qt. Ribbed Pitcher.

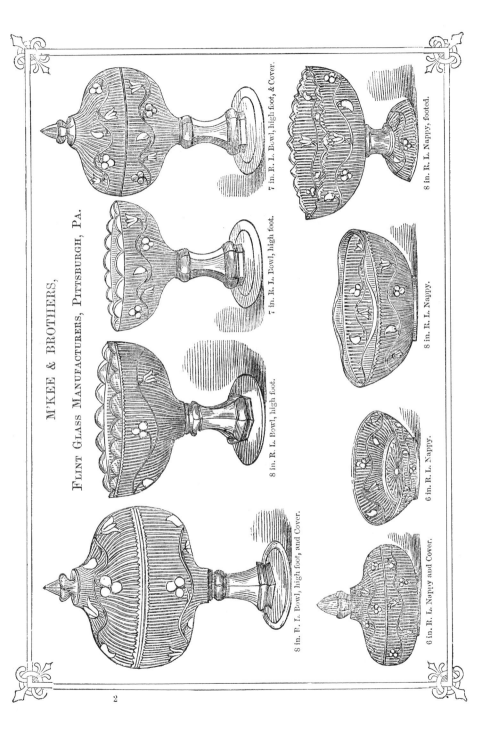

M^cKEE & BROTHERS,

FLINT GLASS MANUFACTURERS, PITTSBURGH, PA.

7 in. R. L. Bowl, high foot, & Cover.

8 in. R. L. Nappy, footed.

7 in. R. L. Bowl, high foot.

8 in. R. L. Nappy.

8 in. R. L. Bowl, high foot.

6 in. R. L. Nappy.

8 in. F. L. Bowl, high foot, and Cover.

6 in. R. L. Nappy and Cover.

2

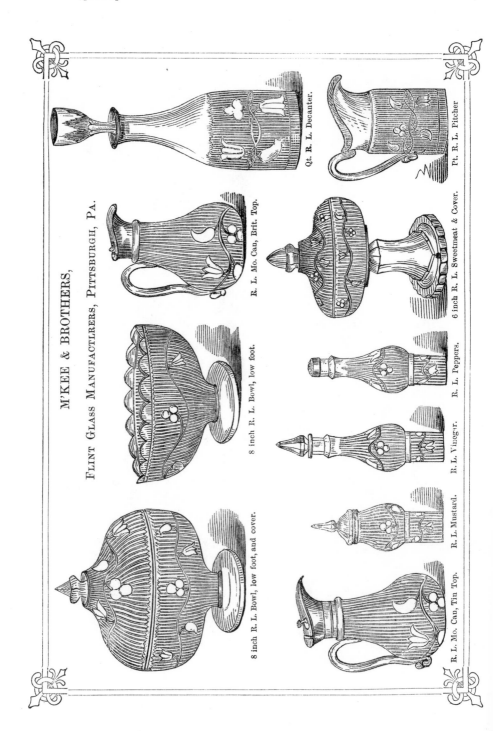

M'KEE & BROTHERS,

FLINT GLASS MANUFACTURERS, PITTSBURGH, PA.

Qt. R. L. Decanter.

Pt. R. L. Pitcher

R. L. Mo. Can, Brit. Top.

6 inch R. L. Sweetmeat & Cover.

8 inch R. L. Bowl, low foot.

R. L. Peppers.

R. L. Vinegr'r.

8 inch R. L. Bowl, low foot, and cover.

R. L. Mustard.

R. L. Mo. Can, Tin Top.

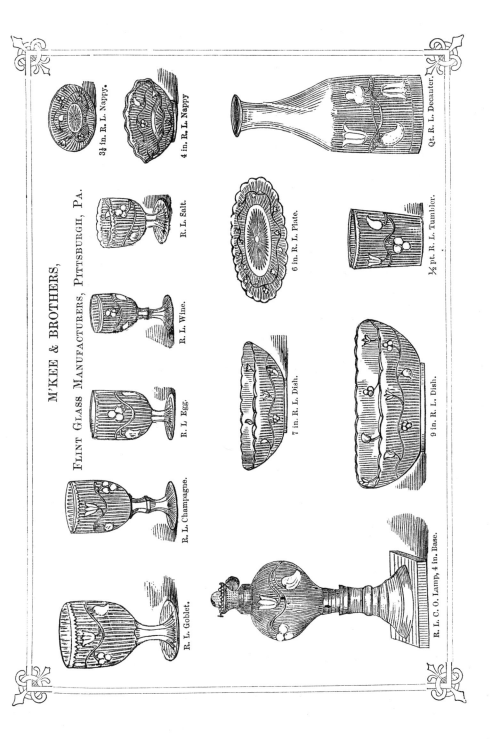

McKEE & BROTHERS,
FLINT GLASS MANUFACTURERS, PITTSBURGH, PA.

3¼ in. R. L. Nappy.

4 in. R. L. Nappy

R. L. Salt.

R. L. Wine.

R. L. Egg.

R. L. Champagne.

R. L. Goblet.

Qt. R. L. Decanter.

6 in. R. L. Plate.

½ pt. R. L. Tumbler.

7 in. R. L. Dish.

9 in. R. L. Dish.

R. L. C. O. Lamp, 4 in. Base.

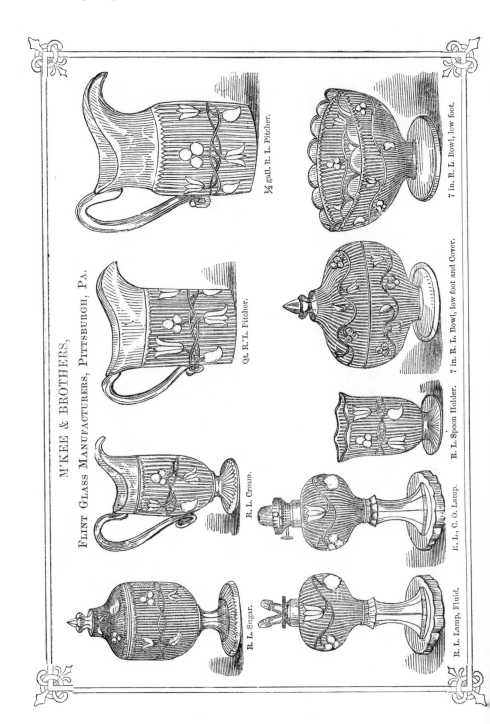

McKEE & BROTHERS,

Flint Glass Manufacturers, Pittsburgh, Pa.

½ gall. R. L. Pitcher.

Qt. R. L. Pitcher.

R. L. Cream.

R. L. Sugar.

7 in. R. L. Bowl, low foot.

7 in. R. L. Bowl, low foot and Cover.

R. L. Spoon Holder.

R. L. C. O. Lamp.

R. L. Lamp, Fluid.

M'KEE & BROTHERS,

Flint Glass Manufactures, Pittsburgh, Pa,

Dolphin Candlestick.

French Candlestick.

Toy Seal Iron.

Toy Tumbler. Toy Candlestick.

½ pt. 10 Flute Jelly Tumbler.

6 Flute Jelly Cup.

Bird Bath.

Diamond Ind. Salt.

Boston Candlestick.

Bird Fountain.

Seed Box.

Butter Print.

Argus Ale.

6 in. Comet Nappy and Cover.

6 in. Comet Sweetmeat and Cover.

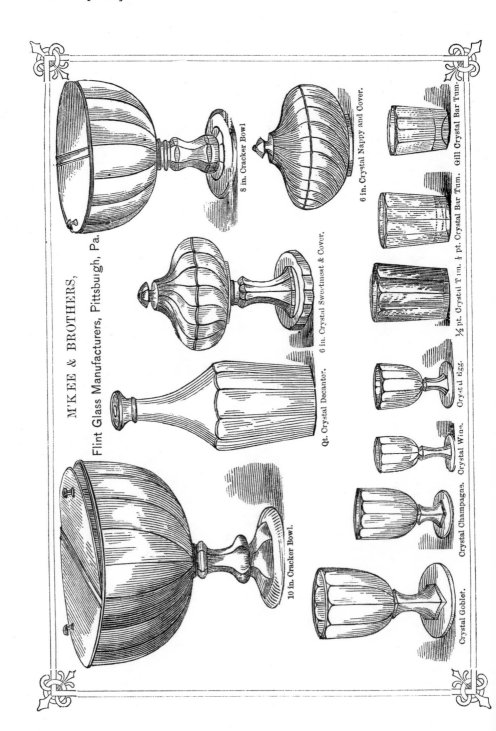

M'KEE & BROTHERS,

Flint Glass Manufacturers, Pittsburgh, Pa.

8 in. Cracker Bowl

6 in. Crystal Nappy and Cover.

Gill Crystal Bar Tum.

6 in. Crystal Sweetmeat & Cover.

Qt. Crystal Decanter.

¼ pt. Crystal Bar Tum.

½ pt. Crystal Tum.

Crystal Egg.

Crystal Wine.

Crystal Champagne.

10 in. Cracker Bowl.

Crystal Goblet.

M'KEE & BROTHERS,

Flint Glass Manufacturers, Pittsburgh.

10 in. Crystal Bowl.

Crystal Spoon Holder.

Crystal Cream.

Crystal Ale.

Qt. Crystal Pitcher.

8 in. Crystal Dish, footed, and Cover.

8 in. Crystal Bowl.

Crystal Celery.

Crystal Sugar.

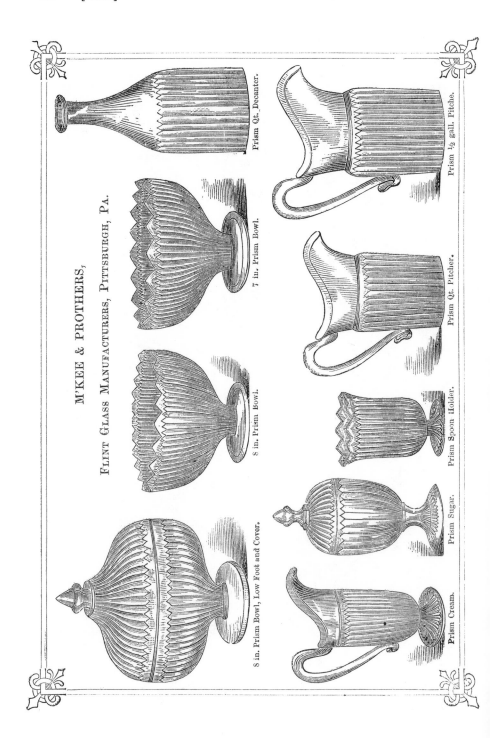

M'KEE & PROTHERS,
FLINT GLASS MANUFACTURERS, PITTSBURGH, PA.

Prism Qt. Decanter.

Prism ½ gall. Pitche.

7 in. Prism Bowl.

Prism Qt. Pitcher.

8 in. Prism Bowl.

Prism Spoon Holder.

8 in. Prism Bowl, Low Foot and Cover.

Prism Sugar.

Prism Cream.

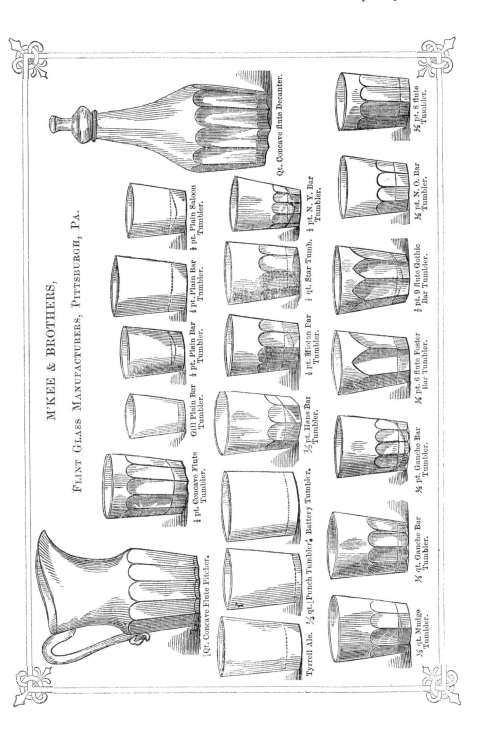

McKEE & BROTHERS,

FLINT GLASS MANUFACTURERS, PITTSBURGH, PA.

Qt. Concave flute Decanter.

½ pt. 8 flute Tumbler.

½ pt. N. O. Bar Tumbler.

⅓ pt. N. Y. Bar Tumbler.

¼ qt. Star Tumb.

⅓ flute Gothic Bar Tumbler.

½ pt. Plain Saloon Tumbler.

½ pt. Plain Bar Tumbler.

1 pt. Mioton Bar Tumbler.

½ pt. 6 flute Foster Bar Tumbler.

Gill Plain Bar Tumbler.

½ pt. Plain Bar Tumbler.

½ pt. Hans Bar Tumbler.

¾ pt. Gauche Bar Tumbler.

½ pt. Concave Flute Tumbler.

½ qt. Gauche Bar Tumbler.

1 Qt. Concave Flute Pitcher.

Tyrrell Ale.

¼ qt. Punch Tumbler.

Battery Tumbler.

¾ qt. Mudge Tumbler.

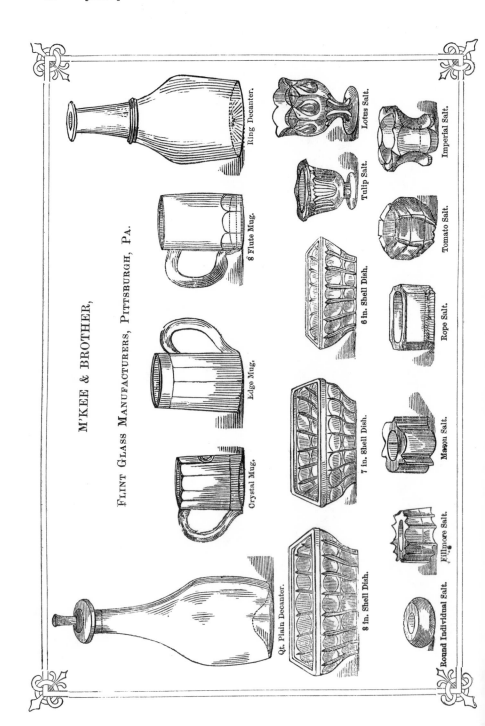

M'KEE & BROTHER,

FLINT GLASS MANUFACTURERS, PITTSBURGH, PA.

Ring Decanter.

8 Flute Mug.

Edge Mug.

Crystal Mug.

Qt. Plain Decanter.

Lotus Salt.

Tulip Salt.

Imperial Salt.

Tomato Salt.

6 in. Shell Dish.

Rope Salt.

7 in. Shell Dish.

Mason Salt.

Fillmore Salt.

8 in. Shell Dish.

Round Individual Salt.

M'KEE & BROTHER,

FLINT GLASS MANUFACTURERS, PITTSBURGH, PA.

Pt. Pillared Syrup Can.

Pt. Fluted Syrup Bottle.

8 in. Oval Mitre Dish.

7 in. Oval Star Dish.

Ex. Jelly.

Ex. Egg.

Ex. Wine.

Ex. Champagne.

Ex. Goblet.

Soap Slab.

Smoke Bell.

Eugenie Mustard.

Eugenie Pepper. Eugenie Vinegar.

Cone Pt'd Mo. Can, Tad top.

Ex. Mo Can, Brit' top.

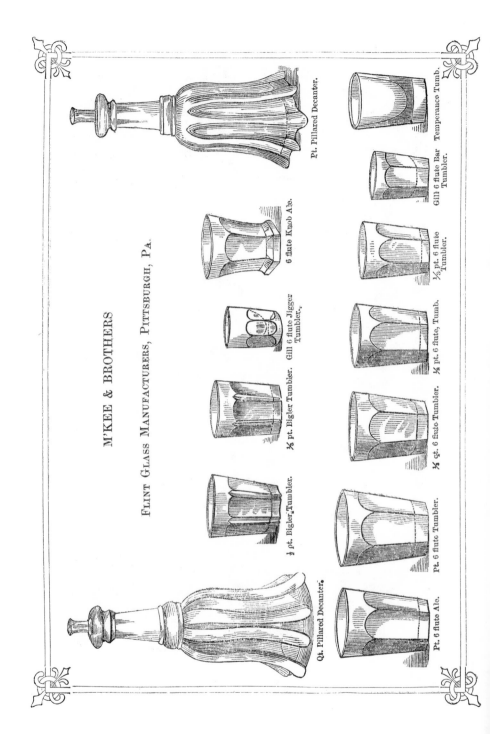

M'KEE & BROTHERS

FLINT GLASS MANUFACTURERS, PITTSBURGH, PA.

Pt. Pillared Decanter.

Temperance Tumb.

Gill 6 flute Bar Tumbler.

½ pt. 6 flute Tumbler.

¾ pt. 6 flute, Tumb.

½ qt. 6 flute Tumbler.

Pt. 6 flute Tumbler.

Pt. 6 flute Ale.

6 flute Knob Ale.

Gill 6 flute Jigger Tumbler.

⅜ pt. Bigler Tumbler.

½ pt. Bigler Tumbler.

Qt. Pillared Decanter.

M'KEE & BROTHERS,
FLINT GLASS MANUFACTURERS, PITTSBURGH, PA.

Ray Celery.

5 in. Ray. Nappy.

Well Inkstand.

7 in. Ray Dish.

6 in. Ray Dish.

Swell Flute Mustard.

Swell Flute Vinegar.

Swell Flute Pepper.

9 in. Ray Dish.

4 in. Ray Nappy.

6 in. Ray Nappy.

Mioton Goblet.

Mioton Champagne.

Ray Sugar.

7 in. Ray Nappy.

Mioton Wine.

Mioton Cordial.

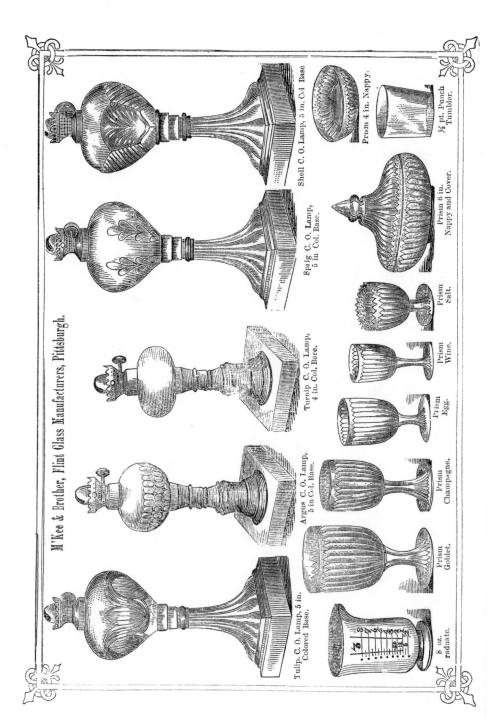

M'Kee & Brother, Flint Glass Manufacturers, Pittsburgh.

Shell C. O. Lamp, 5 in. Col. Base.

Sprig C. O. Lamp, 5 in. Col. Base.

Turnip C. O. Lamp, 4 in. Col. Base.

Argus C. O. Lamp, 5 in Colored Base.

Tulip, C. O. Lamp, 5 in. Colored Base.

Prism 4 in. Nappy.

¾ pt. Punch Tumbler.

Prism 6 in. Nappy and Cover.

Prism Salt.

Prism Wine.

Prism Egg.

Prism Champagne.

Prism Goblet.

8 oz. graduate.

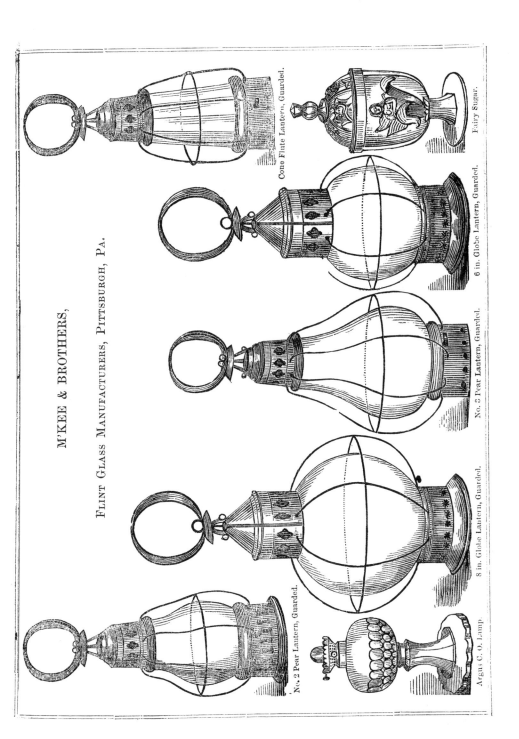

M'KEE & BROTHERS,

FLINT GLASS MANUFACTURERS, PITTSBURGH, PA.

Cone Flute Lantern, Guarded.

Fairy Sugar.

6 in. Globe Lantern, Guarded.

No. 3 Pear Lantern, Guarded.

8 in. Globe Lantern, Guarded.

No. 2 Pear Lantern, Guarded.

Argus C. O. Lamp.

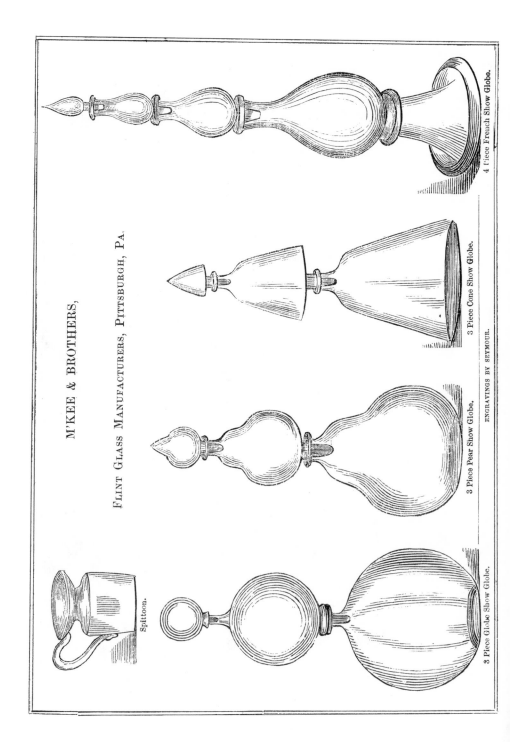

M'KEE & BROTHERS,

FLINT GLASS MANUFACTURERS, PITTSBURGH, PA.

4 Piece French Show Globe.

3 Piece Cone Show Globe.

3 Piece Pear Show Globe.

ENGRAVINGS BY SEYMOUR.

3 Piece Globe Show Globe.

Spittoon.

JULY 1st, 1864.

M'KEE & BROTHERS' PRICE LIST.

TUMBLERS.

	Rough Bottoms.	Ground Bottoms.
Pressed ½ gill Toy......per doz.	45	
Pressed ⅓ pint 6 Flute........"	$1 25	
Pressed ½ pint 6 Flute........"	1 67	$1 82
Pressed ⅓ quart 6 Flute........"		2 33
Pressed pint 6 Flute........"		3 00
Pressed ⅓ quart Excelsior Footed........"		2 80
Pressed ⅓ quart Excelsior Ship........"		2 33
Pressed ½ pint Concave Flute........"	2 15	2 30
Pressed ⅓ quart Mudge........"		2 33
Pressed ½ pint Charleston........"	1 85	2 00
Pressed ½ pint Lind........"	1 33	
Pressed ⅓ quart Band Footed........"		2 80
Pressed ⅓ quart Star........"		2 33
Pressed ⅓ quart Gaines........"		2 67
Pressed ½ pint Crystal........"		2 15
Pressed ⅓ pint 9 Flute Light........"	1 15	
Pressed ½ pint 9 Flute Light........"	1 33	
Pressed ½ pint Eugenie Footed........"		2 33
Pressed ½ pint Finger Flute........"	1 50	1 65
Pressed ⅓ quart Finger Flute........"		2 33
Pressed ½ pint Bigler Flute........"	1 85	2 00
Pressed Temperance........"		10 00
Pressed ½ pint Stedman........"	1 67	1 82
Pressed ½ pint R. L........"		2 13
Pressed ½ pint Mirror........"		2 13
Pressed ½ pint 8 Flute........"	1 40	
Pressed ½ pint Brilliant........"		2 13
Pressed ½ pint Sprig........"		2 13

BAR TUMBLERS.

	Rough Bottoms.	Ground Bottoms.
Pressed gill 6 Flute Bar..................................per doz.	$1 15	$1 30
Pressed ½ pint 6 Flute Foster Bar...................... "		2 15
Pressed gill Plain Bar....................................... "	1 15	1 30
Pressed ⅓ pint Plain Bar................................... "	1 50	1 65
Pressed ½ pint Plain Bar .... "		2 33
Pressed ⅓ pint Plain Saloon Bar.......................... "	1 50	1 65
Pressed ⅓ pint Punch....................................... "		1 85
Pressed ⅛ quart Punch...................................... "		2 33
Pressed ½ pint 9 Flute Bar, extra heavy.............. "		2 33
Pressed ⅓ pint New York Bar.............................. "	1 50	1 65
Pressed ½ pint New Orleans Bar........................... "		2 00
Pressed ½ pint Gothic Bar.................................. "		2 13
Pressed ½ pint Gauche Bar.................................. "		2 13
Pressed ⅓ quart Gauche Bar................................ "		2 33
Pressed ½ pint Mioton Bar.................................. "		2 33
Pressed gill Crystal Bar..................................... "	1 25	1 40
Pressed ⅓ pint Crystal Bar.................... .... "	1 50	1 65
Pressed ½ pint Hans Bar................... .... "		2 40
Pressed gill 6 Flute Jigger.................................. "	1 25	1 40
Pressed gill New York Bar.................................. "	1 25	1 40
Pressed ⅓ pint Gauche Bar..... .... "	1 50	1 65

CHAMPAGNE GLASSES.

Pressed Excelsior.. per doz.	$2 67
Pressed 6 Flute... "	2 67
Pressed Crystal... "	3 00
Pressed R. L. .... "	3 00
Pressed Stedman... "	3 00
Pressed Prism... "	3 00
Pressed Chain... "	3 00
Pressed Brilliant... "	3 00
Pressed Sprig... "	3 00
Pressed New York.. "	3 00
Pressed Mioton Hotel...................................... "	3 00

M'KEE & BROTHERS' PRICES OF GLASS WARE.

ALE AND BEER GLASSES.

Pressed Excelsior Ales, or Long Toms..........................per doz. $3 50		
Pressed 8 Flute Beer Mugs.. "		3 50
Pressed Argus Ales.. "		2 80
Pressed B. V. Beer Mugs... "		3 60
Pressed Crystal Beer Mugs... "		3 50
Pressed small pint 6 Flute Ale Tumblers....................... "		2 80
Pressed ⅛ quart Crystal Ales, Footed .... "		2 80
Pressed 6 Flute Knob Ales.. "		2 33
Pressed Plain Tyrrell Ales .... "		2 33
Pressed ½ pint 10 Flute Ales.. "		2 33
Pressed ⅛ quart 10 Flute Ales..................................... "		2 80
Pressed Edge Beer Mugs.. "		3 50
Pressed Argus Beer Mugs, Ponies .... "		3 00
Pressed Argus Beer Mugs, Large................................. "		3 50
Pressed Cincinnati Beer Mugs...................................... "		3 50
Pressed Ohio Beer Mugs... "		3 50
Pressed Huber Ales... "		3 33
Pressed Poney Tyrrell Ales .... "		2 13
Pressed New York Ales.. "		3 50
Pressed Edge Beer Mugs, Ponies..... .... "		3 00
Pressed 8 Flute Beer Mugs, Ponies............................. "		3 00

DECANTERS.

Pressed pint Excelsior,	and Corks........... per doz.			$8 75
Pressed quart Excelsior,	"	....	"	11 00
Pressed pint Ring Bar,	"	....	"	4 75
Pressed quart Ring Bar,	"	....	"	6 00
Pressed pint Pillar,	"	....	"	14 00
Pressed quart Pillar,	"	....	"	16 50
Pressed quart Concave Flute,	"	....	"	11 00
Pressed quart Crystal,	"	....	"	14 00
Pressed quart R. L. Cut Neck,	"	....	"	20 00
Pressed quart R. L.,	"	....	"	14 00
Pressed quart Stedman,	"	....	"	14 00
Pressed quart Prism,	"	....	"	14 00
Quart Temperance,	"	...........each,		3 00

M'KEE & BROTHERS' PRICES OF GLASS WARE.

WINE GLASSES.

Pressed 6 Flute..per doz.	$1	67
Pressed Excelsior.. "	1	75
Pressed Crystal.. "	1	75
Pressed Mioton Hotel.. "	1	75
Pressed R. L.. "	1	75
Pressed Stedman..... .... "	1	75
Pressed Prism .... "	1	75
Pressed Chain.. "	1	87
Pressed Brilliant... "	1	87
Pressed Sprig.. "	1	87
Pressed New York.. "	1	87

JELLY GLASSES.

Pressed Excelsior..per doz.	$2	13
Pressed 6 Flute Jelly Cups, Footed............................ "	1	75
Pressed ⅓ pint 10 Flute Jelly Tumblers......................... "	1	25
Pressed ½ pint 10 Flute Jelly Tumblers......................... "	1	60

GOBLETS.

Pressed Excelsior..per doz.	$3	25
Pressed 6 Flute... "	3	25
Pressed Crystal... "	3	60
Pressed Mioton Hotel.. "	3	60
Pressed R. L... "	3	60
Pressed Stedman.. "	3	60
Pressed Prism.. "	3	60
Pressed Chain.. "	3	60
Pressed Brilliant... "	3	60
Pressed Sprig.. "	3	60
Pressed New York.. "	3	60

WATER BOTTLES.

Pint Plain..per doz.	$5	00
Quart Plain... "	6	50

M'KEE & BROTHERS' PRICES OF GLASS WARE.

BITTER BOTTLES.

Pressed 6 Flute	per doz. $5 50
Pressed 8 Flute	" 4 50
Pressed Excelsior	" 5 75
Pressed Stedman	" 5 50

LIQUORS AND CORDIALS.

Pressed Mioton Hotel................................per doz. $1 75

PRESSED PLATES.

3 inch Diamond	per doz. $ 36
6 inch Ray	" 1 33
6 inch R. L.	" 1 33
6 inch Stedman	" 1 33
6 inch Sprig	" 1 33

PRESSED CASTER BOTTLES.

Swell Flute, Screw Top	per doz. $1 20
No. 17, "	" 1 20
Eugenie, "	" 1 25
R. L., "	" 1 25
Large Saloon Peppers	" 2 25

MOLASSES CANS.

Pressed pint Pillar Molasses Pitchers, Metal Tops	per doz. $11 00
Pressed Excelsior Molasses Cans, Metal Tops	" 6 25
Pressed Excelsior Molasses Cans, Tin Tops	" 5 00
Pressed No. 14. Molasses Cans, Metal Tops	" 6 25
Pressed No. 14 Molasses Cans, Tin Tops	" 5 00
Pressed Rose Molasses Cans, Metal Tops	" 7 50
Pressed Rose Molasses Cans, Tin Tops	" 6 25
Pressed pint Fine Ribbed Molasses Cans, Glass Stoppers	" 2 75
Pressed Diamond Molasses Cans, Tin Tops	" 5 25
Pressed Diamond Molasses Cans, Metal Tops	" 6 50
Pressed R. L. Molasses Cans, Metal Tops	" 6 50
Pressed R. L. Molasses Cans, Tin Tops	" 5 25
Pressed Stedman Molasses Cans, Metal Tops	" 6 50
Pressed Stedman Molasses Cans, Tin Tops	" 5 25

M'KEE & BROTHERS' PRICES OF GLASS WARE.

CARBON OIL LAMPS.

Pressed Ring Hand...per doz.	$4	75
Pressed Ring Footed.. "	5	75
Pressed Ribbed Footed.. "	5	75
Pressed Ribbed Hand... "	4	75
Pressed Argus Footed.. "	6	25
Pressed Concave Footed... "	6	25
Pressed R. L. Footed.. "	6	25
Pressed Shell Footed.. "	7	25
Pressed Sprig Footed.. "	7	25
Pressed Tulip Footed.. "	7	25
Pressed Vine Footed... "	7	25
Pressed Stedman Footed... "	7	25
Pressed Prism Footed... "	7	25
Pressed Ring 4 inch Colored Base...................................... "	8	50
Pressed Ribbed, 4 inch Colored Base.................................. "	8	50
Pressed Turnip, 4 inch Colored Base.................................. "	8	50
Pressed R. L. 4 inch Colored Base...................................... "	8	50
Pressed Argus, 4 inch Colored Base.................................... "	8	50
Pressed Concave, 4 inch Colored Base................................ "	8	50
Pressed Shell, 5 inch Colored Base.................................... "	11	00
Pressed Sprig, 5 inch Colored Base.................................... "	11	00
Pressed Tulip, 5 inch Colored Base.................................... "	11	00
Pressed Vine, 5 inch Colored Base..................................... "	11	00
Pressed Stedman, 5 inch Colored Base............................... "	11	00
Pressed 3½ inch White Base and Stem................................ "	4	00
Pressed 3½ inch Black Base and Stem................................. "	3	50
Pressed Prism, 5 inch Colored Base.................................... "	11	00
Pressed large Suspension Fountain, No. 1 Burners.............. "	6	50
Pressed large Suspension Fountain, No. 2 Burners.............. "	11	00
Pressed small Suspension Fountain, No. 1 Burners.............. "	5	25
Large Harps for Hanging Lamps, Bronzed......................... "	4	00
Small Harps for Hanging Lamps, Bronzed......................... "	4	00
Small Side Brackets and Reflectors.................................... "	5	00
Large Side Brackets and Reflectors.................................... "	5	00
Pressed Ellipse C. O. Lamps, 5 inch Colored Base.............. "	11	00
Pressed Star and Concave Lamps, 5 inch Colored Base....... "	11	00
Pressed Chain Lamps, 5 inch Colored Base..... .... "	11	00
Pressed Gaines Lamps, 5 inch Colored Base...................... "	11	00
Pressed Cincinnati Lamps, 5 inch Colored Base................. "	11	00
Pressed Assorted Small Pegs, R. L. Concave and Argus...... "	1	75
Pressed Assorted Small Pegs, Ribbed and Ring..... .. .. "	1	70

M'KEE & BROTHERS' PRICES OF GLASS WARE.

CARBON OIL LAMPS.

Pressed Assorted Large Pegs, Ellipse, Star, Concave, Chain,
Gaines, Cincinnati, Shell, Prism, Stedman, Tulip, Sprig,
Vine...per doz. $2 75
Pressed R. L. Footed Lamps, no Burner............................   "   4 00
Pressed Argus Footed Lamps, no Burner.........................   "   4 00
Pressed Concave Footed Lamps, no Burner......................   "   4 00
Pressed Ring Footed Lamps, no Burner ....   "   3 50
Pressed Ribbed Footed Lamps, no Burner.........................   "   3 50
Pressed Large Suspension Fount, No. 1 or No. 2 Mouths....   "   4 00
Pressed Small Suspension Fount, No. 1 Mouth.................   "   3 00
Pressed 4 inch White Base and Stem.............................   "   4 50
Pressed 4 inch Black Base and Stem.............................   "   4 25
Pressed 5 inch White Base and Stem...........................   "   6 00
Pressed 5 inch Black Base and Stem............................   "   5 50
Pressed Ring Hand Lamp, no Burner.............................   "   2 33
Pressed Ribbed Hand Lamp, no Burner..........................   "   2 33

BACON'S BURNERS (for burning without Chimneys), will
be substituted at same price when desired.

CANDLESTICKS.

Pressed French, no Sockets...per doz. $3 50
Pressed Boston, with Sockets...   "   8 00
Pressed Dolphin, with Sockets...   "   7 00
Pressed 6 Flute, no Sockets..   "   4 50

CELERY GLASSES.

Pressed Ray...per doz. $10 00
Pressed Eugenie..   "   8 00
Pressed Crystal...   "   10 67
Pressed Sprig...   "   11 00

M'KEE & BROTHERS' PRICES OF GLASS WARE.

PRESSED DISHES.

6 inch Shell.. per doz.	$2	33
7 inch Shell.. "	3	00
8 inch Shell.. "	4	25
7 inch Oval Star...................................... .... "	2	80
8 inch Oval Mitre.. "	3	87
Shell Pickle.......... .... "	2	67
7 inch Ray... "	3	00
9 inch Ray... "	5	25
7 inch Eugenie Dish, on foot, and Cover...................... "	8	00
9 inch Eugenie Dish, on foot, and Cover...................... "	13	00
9 inch Crystal Dish, on foot, and Cover....................... "	11	00
Shell Sauce.. "	5	50
7 inch R. L.. "	2	87
9 inch R. L.. "	5	25
7 inch Sprig... "	2	87
8 inch Sprig... "	4	00
9 inch Sprig... .... "	5	25

SYRUP CANS AND BOTTLES.

Pressed pint Pillar Syrup Cans.................... ....per doz.	$7	00
Pressed pint Pillar Syrup Bottles.................................... "	5	50
Pressed pint Fluted Syrup Cans........... .... "	5	50
Pressed pint Fluted Syrup Bottles........... .... "	4	00
Pressed pint Plain Syrup Cans .... "	6	00

LANTERNS—Spring Bottoms.

Cone Flute, Oil or Candle..per doz.	$7	00
No. 2 Pear, Oil or Candle...... .... "	7	50
No. 3 Pear, Oil or Candle.. .... "	8	00
Cone Flute, Oil or Candle, Guarded................................ "	8	50
No. 2 Pear, Oil or Candle, Guarded................................ "	9	00
No. 3 Pear, Oil or Candle, Guarded................................ "	9	50
6 inch Globe, Oil or Candle, Guarded .... "	9	00
8 inch Globe, Oil or Candle, Guarded............................. "	16	50

CARBON OIL LANTERNS—Spring Bottoms.

No. 2 Pear, Guarded................................ ....per doz.	$13	00
No. 3 Pear, Guarded...... ... ... "	13	50
6 inch Globe, Guarded.. "	13	00

M'KEE & BROTHERS' PRICES OF GLASS WARE.

LAMP CHIMNEYS.

No. 3 Coal Oil	per doz. $1	50
No. 2 Coal Oil	"	1 20
No. 1 Coal Oil	"	90
No. 1 Coal Oil, Frosted	"	1 10
No. 0 Coal Oil	"	90

SPOON HOLDERS.

Pressed Crystal	per doz. $3	60
Pressed R. L.	"	3 60
Pressed Stedman	"	3 60
Pressed Prism	"	3 60
Pressed Brilliant	"	3 60
Pressed Sprig	"	3 60

EGG GLASSES.

Pressed Excelsior	per doz. $1	75
Pressed Eugenie	"	1 75
Pressed Crystal	"	1 75
Pressed R. L.	"	1 87
Pressed Stedman	"	1 75
Pressed Prism	"	1 75
Pressed Sprig	"	1 87
Pressed New York	"	1 87
Pressed Brilliant	"	1 87

SWEETMEATS—Footed, with Covers.

Pressed 6 inch R. L. and Covers	per doz. $6	50
Pressed 6 inch Crystal and Covers	"	6 50
Pressed 8 inch R. L. Nappies, Footed	"	6 50
Pressed 6½ inch R. L. and Covers	"	7 00
Pressed 6 inch Prism and Covers	"	6 50
Pressed 6 inch Sprig and Covers	"	6 50
Pressed 6 inch Brilliant and Covers	"	6 50

BOWLS FOR HOTELS AND COFFEE HOUSES.

Pressed 8 inch Cracker, Tin Covers	per doz. $20	00
Pressed 10 inch Cracker, Tin Covers	"	25 00

M'KEE & BROTHERS' PRICES OF GLASS WARE.

PRESSED SAUCERS AND NAPPIES.

7 inch Ray Nappies	per doz. $3	00
6 inch Ray Nappies	"	1 87
5 inch Ray Nappies	"	1 33
4 inch Ray Nappies	"	90
6 inch Crystal Nappies	"	2 33
6 inch Crystal Nappies and Covers	"	4 67
8 inch R. L. Nappies	"	5 50
6 inch R. L. Nappies	"	2 33
6 inch R. L. Nappies and Covers	"	4 67
4 inch R. L. Nappies	"	90
3½ inch R. L. Nappies	"	72
6 inch Stedman Nappies	"	2 33
6 inch Stedman Nappies and Covers	"	4 67
6½ inch R. L. Nappies	"	2 75
6½ inch R. L. Nappies and Covers	"	5 50
4 inch Prism Nappies	"	90
6 inch Prism Nappies	"	2 33
6 inch Prism Nappies and Covers	"	4 67
6 inch Sprig Nappies and Covers	"	4 67
6 inch Sprig Nappies	"	2 33
4 inch Sprig Nappies	"	90
6 inch Brilliant Nappies	"	2 33
6 inch Brilliant Nappies and Covers	"	4 67

SUGAR BOWLS AND COVERS.

Pressed Band	per doz. $5	50
Pressed Ray	"	8 00
Pressed Crystal	"	7 00
Pressed R. L.	"	7 00
Pressed Prism	"	7 00
Pressed Brilliant	"	7 00
Pressed Sprig	"	7 00
Pressed S.edman	"	7 00

SALVERS AND CAKE COVERS.

From 6 to 14 inches.................................each 15 cts. per inch.

M'KEE & BROTHERS' PRICES OF GLASS WARE.

PRESSED SALTS.

Pressed Concave..per doz. $ 72
Pressed Fillmore..   "   1 75
Pressed Mason..   "   1 75
Pressed Rope...   "   2 33
Pressed Imperial ....   "   2 33
Pressed Tomato..   "   2 75
Pressed Diamond Individual...................................   "   90
Pressed Tulip...   "   95
Pressed Lotus..   "   2 13
Pressed Diamond..   "   1 40
Pressed Round Individual...   "   90
Pressed R. L..   "   1 40
Pressed Stedman..   "   1 75
Pressed Prism..   "   1 40
Pressed Sprig..   "   1 40

PRESSED BOWLS.

9 inch Concave Bowls.....................................per doz. $12 00
10 inch Excelsior Bowls...................................   "   15 00
10 inch Scollop Diamond Bowls.........................   "   16 50
8 inch Crystal Bowls......................................   "   10 00
10 inch Crystal Bowls.....................................   "   16 50
10 inch Leaf Bowls...   "   15 50
7 inch R. L. Bowls, low foot..............................   "   7 00
7 inch R. L. Bowls, low foot and Covers.............   "   12 00
7 inch R. L. Bowls, high foot............................   "   8 33
7 inch R. L. Bowls, high foot and Covers............   "   13 33
8 inch R. L. Bowls, low foot.............................   "   8 00
8 inch R. L. Bowls, low foot and Covers.............   "   14 00
8 inch R. L. Bowls, high foot............................   "   9 33
8 inch R. L. Bowls, high foot and Covers............   "   15 33
8 inch Stedman Bowls, low foot.........................   "   8 00
8 inch Stedman Bowls, high foot.......................   "   9 33
8 inch Prism Bowls, low foot............................   "   8 00
8 inch Prism Bowls, low foot and Covers............   "   14 00
7 inch Prism Bowls, low foot............................   "   7 00
8 inch Sprig Bowls, low foot............................   "   8 00
8 inch Sprig Bowls, high foot...........................   "   9 33
10 inch Sprig Bowls, high foot.........................   "   18 00
7 inch Sprig Bowls, high foot...........................   "   8 33
7 inch Sprig Bowls, low foot............................   "   7 00
8 inch Brilliant Bowls, low foot........................   "   8 00
8 inch Brilliant Bowls, high foot.......................   "   9 33

11

M'KEE & BROTHERS' PRICES OF GLASS WARE.

PITCHERS AND CREAMS.

Pressed large quart Excelsior..per doz. $8 00
Pressed large pint Excelsior..   "   7 50
Pressed large quart Concave..   "   9 00
Pressed ½ pint Plain Creams ....   "   2 67
Pressed quart Crystal Pitchers..   "   12 00
Pressed ⅓ quart Crystal Creams..   "   5 00
Pressed ½ gallon R. L. Pitchers..   "   16 00
Pressed quart R. L. Pitchers..   "   12 00
Pressed ⅓ quart R. L. Creams..   "   5 00
Pressed ½ gallon Stedman Pitchers ....   "   16 00
Pressed ⅓ quart Stedman Creams..   "   5 00
Pressed ⅓ quart Prism Creams..   "   5 00
Pressed quart Prism Pitchers..   "   12 00
Pressed ½ gallon Prism Pitchers..   "   16 00
Pressed ⅓ quart Brilliant Creams..   "   5 00
Pressed ⅓ quart Sprig Creams..   "   5 00
Pressed ½ gallon Sprig Pitchers..   "   16 00

SUNDRIES.

Pressed Toys..per gross, $4 75
Pressed Bird Fountains....................................per doz. 2 33
Pressed Seed Boxes..   "   1 75
Julep Tubes.......................... ....   "   40
Fish Globes made to order.....................each, from 75 cts. up to 8 00
Shoemakers' Globes....................................per doz. 5 50
Bird Baths..   "   1 75
Butter Prints..   "   3 50
White Enamel Glass Eggs..   "   1 25
Plain Altar Cruets............................. ....   "   15 00
Engraved Altar Cruets...................................... ....   "   20 00
Well Inkstands..   "   5 00
Pressed Soap Slabs......... ....   "   2 13
Pressed Night Lamps, for Fluid.......................................   "   2 33

F. M'KEE'S PATENT FELT WICK, for Carbon Oil.

No. 0, or ⅜ inch wide..per gross, 40 cts.
No. 1, or ⅝ inch wide..   "   50 cts.
No. 2, or 1 inch wide..   "   65 cts.

APOTHECARIES'
SHOP FURNITURE,
MADE OF FLINT GLASS.

Specie Jars, with Tin Japanned Covers.

3 gallon	per doz.	$21 75	½ gallon	per doz.	$5 00
2 gallon	"	13 75	1 quart	"	3 75
6 quart	"	10 50	1 pint	"	2 50
1 gallon	"	7 50	½ pint	"	1 88
3 quart	"	6 25			

Specie Jars, with Tin Japanned Covers.
SQUAT SHAPE.

2 gallon	per doz.	$14 25	1 quart	per doz.	$3 90
1 gallon	"	7 75	1 pint	"	2 63
3 quart	"	6 50	½ pint	"	2 00
½ gallon	"	5 25			

Two Ring Jars, with Glass Covers.

2 gallon	per doz.	$30 00	3 quart	per doz.	$16 50
6 quart	"	25 00	½ gallon	"	14 00
1 gallon	"	20 00	1 quart	"	9 25

Confectionery Jars made to order.   Large Show Jars made to order.

Tinctures, with Ground Crown Stoppers.

2 gallon	per doz.	$15 00	1 quart	per doz.	$4 50
6 quart	"	13 00	1 pint	"	3 00
1 gallon	"	9 25	½ pint and 4 oz	"	2 50
½ gallon	"	6 50	1 and 2 oz	"	2 00

Salt Mouths, with Ground Crown Stoppers.

2 gallon	per doz.	$16 75	1 quart	per doz.	$5 50
6 quart	"	15 00	1 pint	"	4 00
1 gallon	"	11 50	½ pint and 4 oz	"	2 75
½ gallon	"	7 50	1 and 2 oz	"	2 50

M'KEE & BROTHERS' PRICES OF GLASS WARE.

Graduates.

Minimum	per doz.	$6 60
1 oz	"	6 00
2 oz	"	6 60
3 oz	"	7 50
4 oz	"	9 00
6 oz	"	9 60
8 oz	"	12 00
12 oz	"	16 00
16 oz	"	20 00
32 oz	"	33 00

Mortars and Pestles.

Gill	per doz.	$12 00
½ pint	"	13 00
Pint	"	20 00
Quart	"	26 50
½ gallon	"	40 00

Funnels.

Gill	per doz.	$2 00
½ pint	"	2 50
Pint	"	2 75
Quart	"	4 00
½ gallon	"	7 00
Assorted	"	4 00

Syringes.

Pocket Penis	per doz.	$1 20
1 oz. Male, Capped	"	1 25
2 oz. Male, Capped	"	1 50
3 oz. Male, Capped	"	1 75
1 oz. Female, Capped	"	1 50
2 oz. Female, Capped	"	1 75
3 oz. Female, Capped	"	2 00
4 oz. Female, Capped	"	2 50
Curved Womb	"	4 00
Straight Womb	"	4 00
Ear	"	2 00
Eye	"	1 25

M'KEE & BROTHERS' PRICES OF GLASS WARE.

Show Globes.

½ gallon, 2 pieces, Cone or Globe shape..............................each, $1 65
1 gallon, 2 pieces, Cone or Globe shape.............................. "   2 00
2 gallon, 2 pieces, Cone or Globe shape.............................. "   3 25
3 gallon, 3 pieces, Cone or Globe shape.............................. "   5 00
1 gallon, 3 pieces, Pear shape...... .... "   2 75
2 gallon, 3 pieces, Pear shape...... .... "   4 00
3 gallon, 3 pieces, Pear shape....................................... "   6 25
5 gallon, 4 pieces, French style..... .... "   13 00
5 gallon, 3 pieces, French style, engraved, net..................... "   20 00
3 gallon, 3 pieces, French style.................................... "   8 00

Miscellaneous.

Breast Pipes...per doz. $4 15
Nipple Shells... "   1 88
Nursing Bottles... "   4 15
Nipple Shields,... "   3 13
Flat Pessaries.. "   2 50
Globe Pessaries......... .... "   3 30
½, 1 and 2 oz. Cupping Glasses.. "   1 65
Nested Cupping Glasses.. "   2 50
4 oz. Cupping Glasses... "   2 50
8 oz. Cupping Glasses... "   3 33
Glass Speculums... "   5 25
Male and Female Urinals... "   6 25
¼, ½, 1 and 2 drachm Flint Vials..........................per gro.   2 00
Glass Inhalers................. ....per doz. 6 25
Glass Spittoons... "   4 15
Vaccine Glasses... "   5 00
Eye Glasses... "   3 33
Proof Vials... "   2 00

☞ **Glass Tubing, Cane, Spirit Lamps, Electrical Cylinders, Retorts, Receivers, Florence Flasks, together with Chemical and Philosophical Apparatus, all made to order.**

TERMS.

All Bills NET CASH, to be paid within TEN days from date of Invoice.

☞ With the latest improvements, and superior facilities for Manufacturing, we can assure our customers that there is nothing elegant or extra in Flint Glass Ware, made or furnished in this vicinity, but we make and supply.

As we have our Glass put up by experienced packers, in the most neat and careful manner, WE MAKE NO ALLOWANCE FOR BREAKAGE, Bills of Lading being guaranty of good order when shipped.

Do you wish to have your Goods Insured?

We have an open Policy, covering shipments to all points, at as low rates as can be secured here, and include the premium in your merchandise account. Please say INSURE, in all cases where you want the goods covered by us.

UNDATED PRICE LIST

THIS price list is undated, but after study of its contents we feel that it must be from about 1863 or early 1864, the time when the firm had adopted the name M'Kee & Brothers.

The prices in this catalog are about the same as those in 1860 and considerably less than those in the July 1864 catalog. The Civil War period was one of rapidly rising prices, culminating in 1865. In addition, old-fashioned items such as solar and camphene lampshades are included here, as is the "Sprig" pattern patented in May 1863 and other patterns pictured in 1864.

It looks as if 1863–64 was a period of reorganization for M'Kee as well as a period of inflation. This was apparently so serious that it was necessary to go to the expense of printing an entirely new catalog within a year (July 1864) to keep customers aware of the new inventory and higher prices.

PRICES

OF

GLASS WARE

MANUFACTURED BY

M'KEE & BROTHERS,

No. 17 Wood Street, corner of First & Wood Sts.

PITTSBURGH, PA.

ENGRAVINGS BY J. G. SEYMOUR.

PITTSBURGH:
PRINTED BY W. S. HAVEN, CORNER OF WOOD AND THIRD STREETS.

M'KEE & BROTHERS' PRICE LIST.

TUMBLERS.

		Rough Bottoms.	Ground Bottoms.
Pressed ½ gill Toy,	per doz.	27	
Pressed ⅓ pint 6 Flute,	"	70	
Pressed ½ pint 6 Flute,	"	93	$1 06
Pressed ⅓ quart 6 Flute,	"		1 33
Pressed pint 6 Flute,	"	$1 60	1 75
Pressed ⅓ quart Excelsior Footed,	"		1 60
Pressed ⅓ quart Excelsior Ship,	"		1 33
Pressed ½ pint Concave Flute,	"	1 20	1 33
Pressed ⅓ quart Mudge,	"		1 33
Pressed ⅓ pint Charleston,	"	80	93
Pressed ½ pint Charleston,	"	1 00	1 13
Pressed ½ pint Lind,	"	75	
Pressed ⅓ quart Band Footed,	"		1 60
Pressed ⅓ quart Star,	"		1 33
Pressed ⅓ quart Gaines,	"		1 50
Pressed ½ pint Crystal,	"		1 20
Pressed ⅓ pint 9 Flute Light,	"	66	
Pressed ½ pint 9 Flute Light,	"	75	
Pressed ½ pint Eugenie Footed,	"		1 33
Pressed ⅓ pint Finger Flute,	"	72	87
Pressed ½ pint Finger Flute,	"	87	1 00
Pressed ⅓ quart Finger Flute,	"		1 33
Pressed ⅓ pint Bigler Flute,	"	80	93
Pressed ½ pint Bigler Flute,	"	1 00	1 13
Pressed Galvanic Battery, 3½ by 4 inches,	"		3 00
Pressed Temperance,	"		5 00
Pressed ½ pint Stedman,	"	95	1 10
Pressed ½ pint R. L.	"		1 20
Pressed ½ pint Mirror,	"		1 20
Pressed ½ pint 8 Flute,	"	80	
Pressed ½ pint Brilliant,	"		1 20
Pressed ½ pint Sprig,	"		1 20

M'KEE & BROTHERS' PRICES OF GLASS WARE.

BAR TUMBLERS.

		Rough Bottoms.	Ground Bottoms.
Pressed gill 6 Flute Bar,.................................per doz.		66	80
Pressed ½ pint 6 Flute Foster Bar.........................	"		$1 20
Pressed pint 6 Flute Bar,....................................	"	$2 65	2 80
Pressed gill Plain Bar,......................................	"	66	80
Pressed ⅓ pint Plain Bar,...................................	"	87	1 00
Pressed ½ pint Plain Bar,...................................	"		1 33
Pressed ⅓ pint Plain Saloon Bar,...........................	"	87	1 00
Pressed ⅓ pint Punch,......................................	"		1 00
Pressed ⅓ quart Punch,.....................................	"		1 33
Pressed ½ pint 9 Flute Bar, extra heavy,.................	"		1 33
Pressed ⅓ pint New York Bar,.............................	"	87	1 00
Pressed ½ pint New Orleans Bar,..........................	"	1 00	1 13
Pressed ½ pint Gothic Bar,.................................	"		1 20
Pressed ½ pint Gauche Bar,................................	"		1 20
Pressed ⅓ quart Gauche Bar,.............................	"		1 33
Pressed ½ pint Mioton Bar,................................	"		1 33
Pressed gill Crystal Bar,....................................	"	72	87
Pressed ⅓ pint Crystal Bar,................................	"	87	1 00
Pressed ½ pint Hans Bar,....................................	"		1 45
Pressed gill 6 Flute Jigger,.................................	"	72	87
Pressed gill New York Bar,.................................	"	72	87
Pressed ⅓ pint Gauche Bar,................................	"	87	1 00

CHAMPAGNE GLASSES.

Pressed Excelsior,..per doz.		$1 50
Pressed Eugenie,..	"	1 67
Pressed 6 Flute,...	"	1 50
Pressed Crystal,...	"	1 67
Pressed Argus,..	"	1 67
Pressed Mioton Hotel,......................................	"	1 67
Pressed Mirror,..	"	1 67
Pressed R. L.,...	"	1 67
Pressed Stedman,...	"	1 67
Pressed Prism,..	"	1 67
Pressed Chain,..	"	1 67
Pressed Brilliant,...	"	1 67
Pressed Sprig,..	"	1 67
Pressed New York,...	"	1 67

M'KEE & BROTHERS' PRICES OF GLASS WARE.

ALE AND BEER GLASSES.

Pressed Excelsior Ales, or Long Toms,............................per doz.	$2	00
Pressed 8 Flute Beer Mugs,.. "	1	87
Pressed Argus Ales,... "	1	60
Pressed B. V. Beer Mugs,.. "	2	00
Pressed Crystal Beer Mugs,... "	1	87
Pressed small pint 6 Flute Ale Tumblers,............................ "	1	60
Pressed ⅓ quart Crystal Ale, Footed,................................ "	1	60
Pressed 6 Flute Knob Ales,... "	1	33
Pressed Plain Tyrrell Ales,.. "	1	33
Pressed ½ pint 10 Flute Ales,... "	1	33
Pressed ⅓ quart 10 Flute Ales,....................................... "	1	60
Pressed Edge Beer Mugs,... "	2	00
Pressed Argus Beer Mugs, Ponies,.................................... "	1	67
Pressed Argus Beer Mugs, Large,..................................... "	2	00
Pressed Cincinnati Beer Mugs,.. "	2	00
Pressed Ohio Beer Mugs,... "	2	00
Pressed Huber Ales,.. "	1	87
Pressed Poney Tyrrell Ales,... "	1	20
Pressed New York Ales,.. "	2	00
Pressed Edge Beer Mugs, Ponies,..................................... "	1	67

DECANTERS.

Pressed pint Excelsior,	and Corks,...............per doz.		$5	00
Pressed quart Excelsior,	"	....	"	6 33
Pressed quart Gaines,	"	....	"	6 33
Pressed pint Ring Bar,	"	....	"	2 75
Pressed quart Ring Bar,	"	....	"	3 75
Pressed pint Plain Bar,	"	....	"	2 50
Pressed quart Plain Bar,	"	....	"	3 00
Pressed pint Pillar,	"	....	"	8 00
Pressed quart Pillar,	"	....	"	9 33
Pressed quart Concave Flute,	"	....	"	6 33
Cut quart Concave Flute and Cut Neck,	"	....	"	12 00
Pressed quart Crystal,	"	....	"	8 00
Pressed quart R. L.,	"	....	"	8 00
Cut quart R. L.,	"	....	"	12 00
Pressed pint R. L.,	"	....	"	6 67
Pressed quart Stedman, Cup Stoppers,	"	....	"	8 00
Pressed quart Prism,	"	....	"	8 00
Quart Temperance,	"	.... each,		1 50

3

M'KEE & BROTHERS' PRICES OF GLASS WARE.

WINE GLASSES.

Pressed 6 Flute,	per doz. $	95
Pressed Excelsior,	"	1 00
Pressed Eugenie,	"	1 00
Pressed Crystal,	"	1 00
Pressed Mioton Hotel,	"	1 00
Pressed Argus,	"	1 00
Pressed Mirror,	"	1 00
Pressed R. L.,	"	1 00
Pressed Stedman,	"	1 00
Pressed Prism,	"	1 00
Pressed Chain,	"	1 10
Pressed Brilliant,	"	1 10
Pressed Sprig,	"	1 10
Pressed New York,	"	1 10

JELLY GLASSES.

Pressed Excelsior,	per doz. $1	20
Pressed 6 Flute Jelly Cups, Footed,	"	1 00
Pressed ⅓ pint 10 Flute Jelly Tumblers,	"	70
Pressed ½ pint 10 Flute Jelly Tumblers	"	90

GOBLETS.

Pressed Excelsior,	per doz. $1	67
Pressed 6 Flute,	"	1 67
Pressed Eugenie,	"	2 00
Pressed Crystal,	"	2 00
Pressed Mioton Hotel,	"	2 00
Pressed Argus,	"	2 00
Pressed Mirror,	"	2 00
Pressed R. L.	"	2 00
Pressed Stedman,	"	2 00
Pressed Prism,	"	2 00
Pressed Chain,	"	2 00
Pressed Brilliant,	"	2 00
Pressed Sprig,	"	2 00
Pressed New York,	"	2 00

WATER BOTTLES.

Pint Plain	per doz. $3	00
Quart Plain,	"	4 00

4

M'KEE & BROTHERS' PRICES OF GLASS WARE.

BITTER BOTTLES.

Pressed 6 Flute,	per doz.	$3 67
Pressed 8 Flute,	"	3 00
Pressed Excelsior,	"	4 00
Pressed Stedman,	"	3 67

LIQUORS AND CORDIALS.

Pressed Charleston,	per doz. $	95
Pressed Eugenie,	"	1 00
Pressed Mioton Hotel,	"	1 00

PRESSED PLATES.

3 inch Diamond,	per doz.	20
6 inch Ray,	"	72
6 inch R. L.	"	72
6 inch Stedman,	"	72
6 inch Sprig,	"	75

PRESSED CASTER BOTTLES.

Swell Flute,	per doz.	66
No. 17,	"	66
Eugenie,	"	72
R. L. Screw Top,	"	75
Large Saloon Peppers,	"	1 33

MOLASSES CANS.

Pressed pint Pillar Molasses Pitchers, Metal Tops,	per doz.	$6 67
Pressed Excelsior Molasses Cans, Metal Tops,	"	4 00
Pressed Excelsior Molasses Cans, Tin Tops,	"	2 67
Pressed No. 14 Molasses Cans, Metal Tops,	"	4 00
Pressed No. 14 Molasses Cans, Tin Tops,	"	2 67
Pressed Rose Molasses Cans, Metal Tops,	"	4 67
Pressed Rose Molasses Cans, Tin Tops,	"	3 33
Pressed Cone Pillar Molasses Cans, Metal Tops,	"	5 67
Pressed Cone Pillar Molasses Cans, Tin Tops,	"	4 33
Pressed pint Fine Ribbed Molasses Cans, Glass Stoppers,	"	1 50
Pressed Diamond Molasses Cans, Tin Tops,	"	3 00
Pressed Diamond Molasses Cans, Metal Tops,	"	4 33
Pressed R. L. Molasses Cans, Metal Tops,	"	4 33
Pressed R. L. Molasses Cans, Tin Tops,	"	3 00
Pressed Stedman Molasses Cans, Metal Tops,	"	4 33
Pressed Stedman Molasses Cans, Tin Tops,	"	3 00

CARBON OIL LAMPS.

Pressed Ring Hand,	per doz.	$3 67
Pressed Ring Footed,	"	4 00
Pressed Ribbed Footed,	"	4 00
Pressed Ribbed Hand,	"	3 67
Pressed Turnip Footed,	"	4 00
Pressed Argus Footed,	"	4 33
Pressed Concave Footed,	"	4 33
Pressed R. L. Footed,	"	4 33
Pressed Shell Footed,	"	5 00
Pressed Sprig Footed,	"	5 00
Pressed Tulip Footed,	"	5 00
Pressed Vine Footed,	"	5 00
Pressed Stedman Footed,	"	5 00
Pressed Prism Footed,	"	5 00
Pressed Ring, 4 inch Colored Base,	"	6 00
Pressed Ribbed, 4 inch Colored Base,	"	6 00
Pressed Turnip, 4 inch Colored Base,	"	6 00
Pressed R. L., 4 inch Colored Base,	"	6 00
Pressed Argus, 4 inch Colored Base,	"	6 00
Pressed Concave, 4 inch Colored Base,	"	6 00
Pressed Shell, 5 inch Colored Base,	"	8 00
Pressed Sprig, 5 inch Colored Base,	"	8 00
Pressed Tulip, 5 inch Colored Base,	"	8 00
Pressed Vine, 5 inch Colored Base,	"	8 00
Pressed Stedman, 5 inch Colored Base,	"	8 00
Pressed $3\frac{1}{2}$ inch White Base and Stem,	"	2 25
Pressed $3\frac{1}{2}$ inch Black Base and Stem,	"	2 00
Pressed Prism, 5 inch Colored Base,	"	8 00
Pressed large Suspension Fountain, No. 1 Burners,	"	5 33
Pressed large Suspension Fountain, No. 2 Burners,	"	8 00
Pressed small Suspension Fountain, No. 1 Burners,	"	4 00
Large Harps for Hanging Lamps, Bronzed,	"	3 00
Small Harps for Hanging Lamps, Bronzed,	"	3 00
Small Side Brackets and Reflectors,	"	4 00
Large Side Brackets and Reflectors,	"	4 00
Pressed Ellipse C. O. Lamps, 5 inch Colored Base,	"	8 00
Pressed Star and Concave Lamps, 5 inch Colored Base,	"	8 00
Pressed Chain Lamps, 5 inch Colored Base,	"	8 00
Pressed Gaines Lamps, 5 inch Colored Base,	"	8 00
Pressed Cincinnati Lamps, 5 inch Colored Base,	"	8 00
Pressed Assorted Small Pegs, R. L. Concave and Argus,	"	1 00
Pressed Assorted Small Pegs, Ribbed and Ring,	"	95

M'KEE & BROTHERS' PRICES OF GLASS WARE.

CARBON OIL LAMPS.

Pressed Assorted Large Pegs, Ellipse, Star, Concave, Chain,
Gaines, Cincinnati, Shell, Prism, Stedman, Tulip, Sprig,
Vine,..per doz. 1 60
Pressed R. L. Footed Lamps, no Burner,................................ "   2 17
Pressed Argus Footed Lamps, no Burner,............................... "   2 17
Pressed Concave Footed Lamps, no Burner,............................. "   2 17
Pressed Ring Footed Lamps, no Burner,.................................. "   2 00
Pressed Ribbed Footed Lamps, no Burner............................ "   2 00
Pressed Large Suspension Fount, No. 1 or No. 2 Mouths,.... "   2 17
Pressed Small Suspension Fount, No. 1 Mouth,................... "   1 67
Pressed 4 inch White Base and Stem,................................... "   2 67
Pressed 4 inch Black Base and Stem, ... "   2 40
Pressed 5 inch White Base and Stem, ... "   3 67
Pressed 5 inch Black Base and Stem,................................... "   3 33
Pressed Ring Hand Lamp, no Burner,................................... "   1 33
Pressed Ribbed Hand Lamp, no Burner,............................... "   1 33

BACON'S BURNERS (for burning without Chimneys), will be substituted at same prices when desired.

LANTERNS—Common Mountings.

Cone Flute, Oil or Candle,..per doz. $4 33
No. 2 Pear, Oil or Candle, ... "   4 70
No. 3 Pear, Oil or Candle, ... "   5 33
Cone Flute, Oil or Candle, Guarded,................................. "   5 33
No. 2 Pear, Oil or Candle, Guarded,................................. "   6 00
No. 3 Pear, Oil or Candle, Guarded,................................. "   6 67

SMOKE BELLS.

Plain White,...per doz. $8 00
Blue Edge,... "   9 00
Red Edge,.. "   10 00

CANDLESTICKS

Pressed French, no Sockets,...per doz. $2 00
Pressed Boston, with Sockets,... "   4 67
Pressed Dolphin, with Sockets,....................................... "   4 00
Pressed 6 Flute, no Sockets,... "   2 50

CELERY GLASSES.

Pressed Ray,...per doz. $5 33
Pressed Eugenie,.. "   4 50
Pressed Crystal,.. "   6 00
Pressed Sprig,.. "   6 00

M'KEE & BROTHERS' PRICES OF GLASS WARE.

PRESSED DISHES.

6 inch Shell,...per doz.	$1	33
7 inch Shell,..................................... "	1	75
8 inch Shell,...... .... "	2	50
7 inch Oval Star,..................... "	1	60
8 inch Oval Mitre,................. .... "	2	20
Shell Pickle,....................... "	1	50
7 inch Ray,..................................... "	1	67
9 inch Ray,..................................... "	3	00
7 inch Eugenie Dish, on foot,.................. "	3	00
7 inch Eugenie Dish, on foot, and Cover,................ "	4	50
9 inch Eugenie Dish, on foot,.................. "	5	00
9 inch Eugenie Dish, on foot, and Cover,................ "	7	50
8 inch Crystal Dish, on foot,.................. "	4	00
8 inch Crystal Dish, on foot, and Cover,................ "	6	00
Shell Sauce,..................................... "	3	33
7 inch R. L.................................. "	1	60
9 inch R. L.................................. "	3	00
7 inch Sprig,.................................. "	1	60
8 inch Sprig,.................................. "	2	25
9 inch Sprig,.............. .... "	3	50 *n 0*

SYRUP CANS AND BOTTLES.

Pressed pint Pillar Syrup Cans,.................... ....per doz.	$4	00
Pressed pint Pillar Syrup Bottles,................... .... "	3	00
Pressed pint Fluted Syrup Cans,...... ... . "	3	00
Pressed pint Fluted Syrup Bottles,................................ "	2	50
Pressed pint Plain Syrup Cans,................... .... "	3	00 *5 0*

LANTERNS—Spring Bottoms.

Cone Flute, Oil or Candle,............. ....per doz.	$5	75
No. 2 Pear, Oil or Candle,....... .... "	6	00
No. 3 Pear, Oil or Candle,.. .... "	6	67
Cone Flute, Oil or Candle, Guarded,............. .... "	7	00
No. 2 Pear, Oil or Candle, Guarded,.......... .... "	7	50
No. 3 Pear, Oil or Candle, Guarded,.......... .... "	8	67
6 inch Globe, Oil or Candle, Guarded,.......... .... "	8	00
8 inch Globe, Oil or Candle, Guarded,............................ "	13	00

CARBON OIL LANTERNS—Spring Bottoms.

No. 2 Pear, Guarded,.. ....per doz.	$10	00
No. 3 Pear, Guarded,......... .... · .... "	10	67
6 inch Globe, Guarded,......... .... "	10	00

M'KEE & BROTHERS' PRICES OF GLASS WARE.

LAMP CHIMNEYS.

2 inch, $2\frac{1}{8}$, $2\frac{3}{8}$, $2\frac{1}{4}$ and $2\frac{1}{2}$ inch Solar,..........per doz.	$1 00
2 inch Camphene,.......... "	1 75
$2\frac{3}{4}$ inch and 3 inch Camphene,.......... "	2 00
$3\frac{1}{4}$ inch and $3\frac{1}{2}$ inch Camphene,.......... "	2 25
$3\frac{1}{2}$ inch Turn-over Globes,.......... "	4 00
No. 2, Coal Oil,.......... "	87
No. 1, Coal Oil,.......... "	67
No. 1, Coal Oil, Frosted,.......... "	87
No. 0, Coal Oil.......... "	67

SPOON HOLDERS.

Pressed Crystal,..........per doz.	$2 00
Pressed R. L.......... "	2 00
Pressed Stedman,.......... "	2 00
Pressed Prism, ... "	2 00
Pressed Brilliant,.......... "	2 00
Pressed Sprig,.......... "	2 00

EGG GLASSES.

Pressed Excelsior,..........per doz.	$1 00
Pressed Eugenie, ... "	1 00
Pressed Crystal, ... "	1 00
Pressed R. L... .... "	1 10
Pressed Stedman, ... "	1 00
Pressed Prism, ... "	1 00
Pressed Sprig, ... "	1 10
Pressed New York, ... "	1 10
Pressed Brilliant, ... "	1 10

SWEETMEATS, Footed, with Covers.

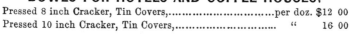

Pressed 7 inch Leaf and Covers,..........per doz.	$4 75
Pressed $7\frac{1}{2}$ inch Tulip and Covers,.......... "	5 00
Pressed $5\frac{1}{2}$ inch Tulip and Covers,.......... "	3 50
Pressed 6 inch Comet and Covers,.......... "	3 75
Pressed 6 inch R. L. and Covers,.......... "	4 00
Pressed 6 inch Crystal and Covers,.......... "	4 00
Pressed 8 inch R. L. Nappies, Footed,.......... "	4 00
Pressed $6\frac{1}{2}$ inch R. L. and Covers,.......... "	4 33
Pressed 6 inch Prism and Covers,.......... "	4 00
Pressed 6 inch Sprig and Covers,.......... "	4 00
Pressed 6 inch Brilliant and Covers, ... "	4 00

BOWLS FOR HOTELS AND COFFEE HOUSES.

Pressed 8 inch Cracker, Tin Covers,..........per doz.	$12 00
Pressed 10 inch Cracker, Tin Covers,.......... "	16 00

M'KEE & BROTHERS' PRICES OF GLASS WARE.

PRESSED SAUCERS AND NAPPIES.

3½ inch Star Nappies,	per doz. $	40
6 inch Comet Nappies,	"	1 33
6 inch Comet Nappies and Covers,	"	2 50
7 inch Leaf Nappies,	"	1 67
7 inch Leaf Nappies and Covers,	"	3 00
7 inch Ray Nappies,	"	1 75
6 inch Ray Nappies,	"	1 10
5 inch Ray Nappies,	"	75
4 inch Ray Nappies,	"	50
6 inch Crystal Nappies,	"	1 33
6 inch Crystal Nappies and Covers,	"	2 67
8 inch R. L. Nappies	"	3 00
6 inch R. L. Nappies,	"	1 33
6 inch R. L. Nappies and Covers,	"	2 67
4 inch R. L. Nappies,	"	50
3½ inch R. L. Nappies,	"	40
6 inch Stedman Nappies,	"	1 33
6 inch Stedman Nappies and Covers,	"	2 67
6½ inch R. L. Nappies,	"	1 67
6½ inch R. L. Nappies and Covers,	"	3 00
4 inch Prism Nappies,	"	50
6 inch Prism Nappies,	"	1 33
6 inch Prism Nappies and Covers,	"	2 67
6 inch Sprig Nappies and Covers,	"	2 67
6 inch Sprig Nappies,	"	1 33
4 inch Sprig Nappies,	"	50
6 inch Brilliant Nappies,	"	1 33
6 inch Brilliant Nappies and Covers,	"	2 67

SUGAR BOWLS AND COVERS.

Pressed Band pattern,	per doz. $3	00
Pressed Eugenie pattern,	"	4 00
Pressed Ray Pattern,	"	4 50
Pressed Crystal,	"	4 00
Pressed R. L.	"	4 00
Pressed Prism,	"	4 00
Pressed Brilliant,	"	4 00
Pressed Sprig,	"	4 00
Pressed Diamond,	"	4 00
Pressed Stedman,	"	4 00

SALVERS AND CAKE COVERS.

From 6 to 14 inches, each, 10 cts. per inch.

M'KEE & BROTHERS' PRICES OF GLASS WARE.

PRESSED SALTS.

Pressed Concave,..................per doz.	$	40
Pressed Fillmore,.......................... "	1	00
Pressed Mason,............................. "	1	00
Pressed Rope,.............................. "	1	33
Pressed Imperial,.......................... "	1	33
Pressed Tomato,........................... "	1	60
Pressed Diamond Individual,........... "		50
Pressed Tulip,.............................. "		54
Pressed Lotus,............................. "	1	20
Pressed Diamond,......................... "		80
Pressed Round Individual,............... "		50
Pressed R. L............................... "		80
Pressed Stedman,......................... "	1	00
Pressed Prism,............................. "		80
Pressed Sprig,............................. "		80

PRESSED BOWLS.

9 inch Concave Bowls,..............per doz.	$7	33
10 inch Excelsior Bowls,................. "	9	00
10 inch Scollop Diamond Bowls,......... "	10	00
8 inch Crystal Bowls,..................... "	6	00
10 inch Crystal Bowls,................... "	10	00
10 inch Leaf Bowls,...................... "	9	33
7 inch R. L. Bowls, low foot,............ "	4	00
7 inch R. L. Bowls, low foot and Covers,.... "	7	33
7 inch R. L. Bowls, high foot,........... "	5	33
7 inch R. L. Bowls, high foot and Covers,.... "	8	00
8 inch R. L. Bowls, low foot,............ "	5	00
8 inch R. L. Bowls, low foot and Covers,.... "	8	67
8 inch R. L. Bowls, high foot,........... "	6	00
8 inch R. L. Bowls, high foot and Covers,.... "	9	33
8 inch Stedman Bowls, low foot,......... "	5	00
8 inch Stedman Bowls, high foot,........ "	6	00
8 inch Prism Bowls, low foot,........... "	5	00
8 inch Prism Bowls, low foot and Covers,.... "	8	67
7 inch Prism Bowls, low foot,........... "	4	00
8 inch Sprig Bowls, low foot,........... "	5	00
8 inch Sprig Bowls, high foot,........... "	6	00
10 inch Sprig Bowls, high foot,......... "	11	00
7 inch Sprig Bowls, high foot,........... "	5	33
7 inch Sprig Bowls, low foot,........... "	4	00
8 inch Brilliant Bowls, low foot,........ "	5	00
8 inch Brilliant Bowls, high foot,........ "	6	00

M'KEE & BROTHERS' PRICES OF GLASS WARE.

PITCHERS AND CREAMS.

Pressed large quart Excelsior,...per doz.	$5	33
Pressed large pint Excelsior,... "	4	00
Pressed large quart Gaines,.. "	5	33
Pressed large quart Concave,... "	5	33
Pressed ½ pint Plain Creams,... "	1	50
Pressed quart Ribbed Pitchers,....................................... "	3	33
Pressed quart Crystal Pitchers,...................................... "	7	33
Pressed ⅓ quart Crystal Creams,...................................... "	3	00
Pressed ½ gallon R. L. Pitchers,...................................... "	8	67
Pressed quart R. L. Pitchers,... "	7	33
Pressed pint R. L. Pitchers,.. "	5	33
Pressed ⅓ quart R. L. Creams,... "	3	00
Pressed ½ gallon Stedman Pitchers,.................................... "	8	67
Pressed quart Stedman Pitchers,............... .... "	7	33
Pressed ⅓ quart Stedman Creams,...................................... "	3	00
Pressed ⅓ quart Prism Creams,... "	3	00
Pressed quart Prism Pitchers,... "	7	33
Pressed ½ gallon Prism Pitchers,...................................... "	8	67
Pressed ⅓ quart Brilliant Creams,..................................... "	3	00
Pressed ⅓ quart Sprig Creams,... "	3	00
Pressed ½ gallon Sprig Pitchers,...................................... "	8	67

SUNDRIES.

Pressed Toys,...per gross,	$2	70
Pressed Bird Fountains,...per doz.	1	33
Pressed Seed Boxes, ... "	1	00
Julep Tubes,.. "		20
Fish Globes made to order,...................each, from 50 cents up to 5		00
Shoemakers' Globes,..per doz.	3	00
Bird Baths,... "	1	00
Butter Prints,...................... .... "	2	00
White Enamel Glass Eggs,.......... .... "		67
Plain AltarC ruets,... "	12	00
Engraved Altar Cruets,.. "	18	00
Well Inkstands,... "	3	00
Pressed Soap Slabs,... "	1	20
Pressed Night Lamps, for Fluid,..................... .. .. "	1	33

F. M'KEE'S PATENT FELT WICK, for Carbon Oil.

No. 0, or ⅜ inch wide,...per gross,	40 cts.
No. 1, or ⅝ inch wide,... "	50 cts.
No. 2, or 1 inch wide,.. "	65 cts.
No. 3, or 1½ inch wide,...... .... "	$1 00

APOTHECARIES'
SHOP FURNITURE,
MADE OF FLINT GLASS.

Specie Jars, with Tin Japanned Covers.

3 gallon,..............per doz. $13 25	½ gallon,..............per doz. $3 00
2 gallon,................. " 8 25	1 quart,................. " 2 25
6 quart,................ .. " 6 50	1 pint,.................. " 1 50
1 gallon,................. " 4 75	½ pint,.................. " 1 15
3 quart,................ . " 3 75	

Specie Jars, with Tin Japanned Covers.
SQUAT SHAPE.

2 gallon,.. ....per doz. $8 75	1 quart,.................per doz. $2 40
1 gallon,................ " 5 00	1 pint,.................. " 1 60
3 quart,................ .. " 4 00	½ pint,.................. " 1 25
½ gallon,................ " 3 13	

Two Ring Jars, with Glass Covers.

2 gallon,............ ..per doz. $18 00	3 quart.................per doz. $10 00
6 quart,............. ... " 15 00	½ gallon,.............. " 8 50
1 gallon,............... " 12 00	1 quart,................ " 5 75
Confectionery Jars made to order.	Large Show Jars made to order.

Tinctures, with Ground Crown Stoppers.

2 gallon,............ ...per doz. $9 25	1 quart,.................per doz. $2 75
6 quart,............... .. " 8 00	1 pint,.................. " 2 00
1 gallon,................ " 5 75	½ pint and 4 oz........ " 1 50
½ gallon,.. .... " 4 00	1 and 2 oz............. " 1 25

Salt Mouths, with Ground Crown Stoppers.

2 gallon,..............per doz. $11 00	1 quart,.................per doz. $3 50
6 quart,............. ... " 9 00	1 pint,.............. ... " 2 25
1 gallon,...... .... " 7 00	½ pint and 4 oz....... . " 1 75
½ gallon,................ " 4 50	1 and 2 oz............. " 1 50

M'KEE & BROTHERS' PRICES OF GLASS WARE.

Graduates.

Minimum,	per doz. $4 20
1 oz.,	" 3 60
2 oz.,	" 4 20
3 oz.,	" 4 80
4 oz.,	" 5 40
6 oz.,	" 6 00
8 oz.,	" 7 20
12 oz.,	" 9 00
16 oz.,	" 12 00
32 oz.,	" 21 00

Mortars and Pestles.

Gill,	per doz. $ 9 00
½ pint,	" 10 00
Pint,	" 15 00
Quart,	" 20 00
½ gallon,	" 30 00

Funnels.

Gill,	per doz. $1 25
½ pint,	" 1 50
Pint,	" 1 75
Quart,	" 2 50
½ gallon,	" 4 00
Assorted,	" 2 50

Syringes.

Pocket Penis,	per doz. $1 00
1 oz. Male, Capped,	" 1 25
2 oz. Male, Capped,	" 1 50
3 oz. Male, Capped,	" 1 75
1 oz. Female, Capped,	" 1 50
2 oz. Female, Capped,	" 1 75
3 oz. Female, Capped,	" 2 00
4 oz. Female, Capped,	" 2 50
Curved Womb,	" 4 00
Straight Womb,	" 4 00
Ear,	" 2 00
Eye,	" 1 25

K'KEE & BROTHERS' PRICES OF GLASS WARE.

Show Globes.

½ gallon, 2 pieces, Cone or Globe shape,...........................each, $1 00
1 gallon, 2 pieces, Cone or Globe shape,............................. "   1 25
2 gallon, 2 pieces, Cone or Globe shape,............................. "   2 00
3 gallon, 3 pieces, Cone or Globe shape,............................. "   3 00
1 gallon, 3 pieces, Pear shape,.. "   1 75
2 gallon, 3 pieces, Pear shape,.. "   2 75
3 gallon, 3 pieces, Pear shape,.. "   3 50
5 gallon, 4 pieces, French style,... "   8 00
5 gallon, 3 pieces, French style, engraved, net,...................... "   12 00
3 gallon, 3 pieces, French style,... "   5 00

Druggists' Specimen Bottles.

Quarts,...per doz. $6 00
Pints,... "   4 00
½ Pints,... "   3 50
4 ounce,... "   3 00

Miscellaneous.

Breast Pipes,...per doz. $2 50
Nipple Shells,.. "   1 25
Nursing Bottles,... "   2 50
Nipple Shields,.. "   2 00
Flat Pessaries,... "   1 50
Globe Pessaries,... "   2 00
½, 1 and 2 oz. Cupping Glasses,............................... "   1 00
Nested Cupping Glasses,... "   1 50
4 oz. Cupping Glasses,.. "   1 50
8 oz. Cupping Glasses, ... "   2 00
Glass Speculums,... "   3 25
Male and Female Urinals,.. "   3 75
¼, ½, 1 and 2 drachm Flint Vials,..................per gro.   2 00
Glass Inhalers,..per doz.   3 75
Glass Spittoons,... "   2 50
Vaccine Glasses,.. "   3 75
Eye Glasses,.. "   2 00
Proof Vials,... "   1 25

☞**Glass Tubing, Cane, Spirit Lamps, Electrical Cylinders, Retorts, Receivers, Florence Flasks, together with Chemical and Philosophical Apparatus, all made to order.**

TERMS.

All Bills NET CASH, to be paid within TEN days from date of Invoice.

With the latest improvements, and superior facilities for Manufacturing, we can assure our customers that there is nothing elegant or extra in Flint Glass Ware, made or furnished in this vicinity, but we make and supply.

As we have our Glass put up by experienced packers, in the most neat and careful manner, WE MAKE NO ALLOWANCE FOR BREAKAGE, Bills of Lading being guarantee of good order when shipped.

Do you wish to have your Goods Insured?

We have an open Policy, covering shipments to all points at as low rates as can be secured here, and include the premium in your merchandise account.   Please say INSURE, in all cases where you want the goods covered by us.

THE 1868 CATALOG

I NEVITABLY a comparison will be drawn between the 1864 and the 1868 catalogs. After repeated study it is apparent that the 1864 book is more valuable for the collector and that of 1868 more worthwhile for the historian. In the earlier catalog there are 13 pages with displays of eight pressed patterns of tableware: four Ribbed Leaf (Bellflower), two Crystal, two Sprig and one each for Brilliant, Eugenie, Excelsior, Prism and Stedman—an excellent range of forms in single designs. In the 1868 catalog only nine pages show arrangements of six pressed tableware patterns: two Crystal, two N.P.L. (New Pressed Leaf), two of Sprig, one each of Eugenie, Eureka, and Excelsior.

Since the 1868 catalog has more patterns pictured, 74 instead of the 56 in the 1864 catalog, the student may surmise that increased production is reflected. Certainly, the later catalog also reveals effective merchandizing and offerings in the area of sundries. It also shows how isolated forms can impress the potential customer and make his selection easier.

A digression at this point about other catalogs may be helpful. J. B. Lyon, in an 1861 catalog of the O'Hara Flint Glass Works in a private collection, uses the method of categorizing by forms. The first two pages show 63 tumblers and mugs. Page three pictures goblets and stemware with five patterns in 45 pieces. Such a display is not too tiresome, but when 23 Cincinnati bowls occupy a whole page, the reader's attention flags. When Lyon presents 28 footed nappies bearing 12 different patterns, one can learn a great deal through the comparison. Throughout the 19 pages Lyon arranged his material according to form, except for a page, headed Sugars, Creams & Spoon Holders, which presents O'Hara, Cincinnati, Genella, and Crystal in what appears to be the traditional set of four pieces. The covered butter is omitted in each group. In the catalogs of the sixties, the covered nappy is usually placed as a butter dish, although the term "butter" is not used. M'Kee does not use the word butter in any of the catalogs reproduced here.

In the Bakewell, Pears catalog (ca. 1875) four-piece sets do not include the covered nappy by name, but it is in the butter dish position. On other pages, however, a flanged butter dish in the Icicle pattern and footed butters in Victoria and Argus patterns, without covers, are shown.[14]

A King & Son catalog in the Corning Museum Library, ca. 1875, uses the term "covered nappy" most of the time. Nevertheless, the Gothic pattern shows the same form, which is referred to as a butter dish. Elsewhere, No. 13 and No. 14 present "flanged" and "footed butter dishes."[15] We must conclude that in the 1870s butter dishes were just becoming fashionable as a form, and the companies and their customers were in a state of transition.

The M'Kees did not use the featured form until 1868, and the arrangement strengthened their advertising. Goblets and wines, condiment bottles, syrup or molasses cans, mugs, tumblers, and show globes are examples. Closely allied to this advertising style are the pages that *almost* qualify: seven decanters and two suspension lamps; five lamps and four Ray dishes; eight lamps and one base; five lanterns, one sugar and one lamp; five decanters and three Shell dishes. The mixture is undeniably attractive.

The Lyon catalog has an order form opposite each page of pictures, a very businesslike arrangement. The M'Kee catalogs may make the potential customer shuffle pages a bit, but he is repaid by seeing a great variety of forms in one pattern. The Lyon catalog does not explore a single pattern *per se*.

M'Kee's isolation of the molasses cans or syrups presents an opportunity to mention techniques other than pressing. Diamond, Rose, and No. 14 are clearly mold-blown. Fine Ribbed, particularly with the acorn stopper, is a favorable item for Midwestern collectors. The strong lines at the top fading away toward the base bespeak pattern molding. The M'Kees labeled one Pillared Mo. pitcher, to identify pillar molding. Ribbed Leaf (Bellflower), Excelsior, and Stedman probably represent a form of mold-blowing. All have applied handles as do nearly all of the handled pieces in the catalog.

It is to be expected that the M'Kee 1868 catalog would have identical pages taken from the 1864. Two pages of Sprig and one each of Crystal, Eugenie, and Excelsior underscore the popularity of the styles. The M'Kees did not need to reproduce the whole page. For instance, the 1864 catalog showed five lamps, five pieces of Prism stemware and two Prism nappies, a graduate, and a punch tumbler on one page. In

[14] *Bakewell Catalog*, p. 46.
[15] King, Son & Co., Cascade Glass Works, catalog, cà. 1875. Coll: The Corning Museum of Glass, n.p.

the 1868 edition, the same five lamps became the top row above four open dishes of the Ray pattern, an improved grouping.

Designers in the sixties were conservative. Crystal, which relates directly to Huber and Flute, appeared at several factories. Excelsior and Eugenie, more graceful forms than the stiff cut glass, represented geometric designs. N.P.L. (New Pressed Leaf) was a less stylized version of R.L. (Ribbed Leaf), omitting the ribbing.

Brilliant (1864), along the lines of Excelsior and Eugenie, had been reduced to one piece in 1868; R.L. (Bellflower), 42 pieces in 1864, numbered only seven in 1868; N.P.L. (23 pieces) may have been introduced in 1868 as a substitute for R.L. Eureka was added for novelty. Over the 1855–70 period, basic designs, slightly changed, were used for new issues: Honeycomb (New York, Vernon, Cincinnati); Argus (Thumbprint/, Almond Thumbprint, Diamond Thumbprint, Light Thumbprint). At the same time some pattern names persisted: Huber, Loop, Flute, Crystal, and Prism. We do not know all the factories that may have produced these patterns under a different name, perhaps, or with slight variations. That is why glass-factory catalogs are so valuable for documentation.

Certain pressed designs with variations—Diamond, Flute, and Concave—appear regularly in the M'Kee catalog from 1860 on. There is no evidence that M'Kee made complete sets in these patterns, though the designs provided basic starting points. Other patterns were pictured in some forms because they were popular among glassmakers. Leaf, or Loop as it was called in the East, appeared in a 10″ compote, a 7″ sweetmeat and cover, and a 7″ nappy and cover. Such Leaf pieces were also made at the Lyon factory in Pittsburgh as well as in the East. The Comet nappy and cover, and the sweetmeat and cover were shown regularly. A printer's error in 1868 reversed the pattern names under Leaf and Comet, a mistake confusing to modern collectors. The Gaines pitcher and lamp reveal different forms. Shell would seem functionally to be an open dish, yet the pattern was used also for a lamp. Band, as a footed tumbler, retained its popularity. The name Argus appears attached to two entirely different patterns, one only on stemware and another (present-day Thumbprint) on other pieces. This usage is consistent in all four catalogs. One wonders if any of the above designs were ever produced as a complete set. M'Kee's limited use of them is known, but perhaps other manufacturers only chose forms that would best serve their public.

In the seventies different design techniques were added: true naturalism, frosting, and etching. There is also an increase in the number of forms.

The number of lighting devices and their types scarcely vary from

1864 to 1868. There are still two carbon-oil hand lamps, a night lamp for fluid, and a separate 3″ base which seems to have a brass stem. The other lamps shown are all coal lamps with pressed fonts, most of them made in patterns matching the pressed glass dishes and stemware in the catalog. Many of the lamps can be obtained with two different styles of bases: a pressed stem which is obviously attached to the font by a wafer, and a square foot and glass stem attached to the font with a brass collar. This situation was true in 1864 as well. Several lamps are listed as being available with colored bases, the only mention of color in any of these catalogs. It may be that "colored base" indicates a marble or stoneware base as these do appear, and "footed" is the M'Kee designation for a glass base. The lamp patterns available are Vine, Stedman, Prism, Shell, R.L., Tulip, Ribbed, Ring Concave, Argus, and Sprig. There is one lamp which is probably blown or mold-blown: a turnip lamp with a plain undecorated font. The five lanterns and the four candlesticks vary hardly at all from the previous two catalogs.

There are quite a few blown druggists' sundries offered in these catalogs; the show globes are even more elaborate in 1868, and although not illustrated, many sundries listed in the price list emphasize that these are made of flint glass, although the catalog is titled *M'Kee & Brothers Flint Glass Manufacturers*. Perhaps the emphasis on flint glass for the blown wares may indicate that pressed glass was by this time made of the soda-lime formula which had been introduced in 1864. It is impossible to tell when, if at all, M'Kee might have switched formulas for its pressed tableware. Most of the pieces which have been examined appear to be flint glass. However, it seems likely that M'Kee must have made the switch along with other Pittsburgh companies in order to remain competitive.

Items mentioned in the Price List but never illustrated in the catalogs are altar cruets and vases. There may not have been a market for these to justify the cost of illustrations. Ring jars, show globes, and miscellaneous items such as breast pipes, nursing bottles, nipple shells, and cupping glasses were also included in the price list and not illustrated. Glass spittoons and eyeglasses were also available.

PICTURED IN THE 1868 CATALOG

PATTERN	NUMBER OF PIECES	PATTERN	NUMBER OF PIECES
Argus—3 Type 1		Band	3
—3 Type 2	6	Boston candlestick	1

PATTERN	NUMBER OF PIECES	PATTERN	NUMBER OF PIECES
Brilliant	1	Pillared	5
Cincinnati	3	Plain	3
Comet	2	Prism	9
Concave	3	Ray	6
Concave Flute	2	Ribbed	4
Crystal	21	Ribbed, Fine	1
Diamond	2	Ribbed Leaf	7
Diamond & Oval	1	Ring	3
Dolphin candlestick	1	Rope	1
		Rose	1
Eugenie	13		
Eureka	8	Shell	7
Excelsior	15	Sprig	20
Fairy	1	Stedman	9
Fillmore	1	Temperance	1
Flute, N.O.	1	Tomato	1
Flute, Six	5	Tulip	3
Flute, Eight	1	Turnip	2
Flute, Nine	1	Tyrrell	3
Flute, Swelled	3	Vine	2
Fluted	2		
French candlestick	1		

TUMBLERS

PATTERN	NUMBER OF PIECES
Gaines	4
Astor	1
Huber	1
Concave	1
Imperial	1
Flute, Six-Foster	1
Flute, Eight	1
Leaf	2
Flute, Nine	1
Lotus	1
Flute, Nine-Gothic	1
Mason	1
Gaines	1
Mioton	4
Gauche	3
Mirror	4
Hales	1
Morton	1
Lind	1
Mioton	1
Number 14	1
Mirror	1
Number 17	3
Mudge	1
N.P.L. (New Pressed Leaf)	23
New York	2
Oval Mitre	1
Plain	4
Oval Star	1
Star	1

PRICES OF GLASS WARE

Manufactured by

M'KEE & BROTHERS,

No. 17 Wood Street, corner of Wood and First,

PITTSBURGH, PA.

April 1st, 1868.

PRINTED BY W. S. HAVEN, CORNER OF WOOD AND THIRD STREETS, PITTSBURGH.

APRIL 1st, 1868.

———o———

M'Kee & Brothers' Price List.

———o———

TUMBLERS.

		Rough Bottoms.	Ground Bottoms.
Pressed ½ gill Toy, ...per doz.		40	
Pressed ⅓ pint 6 Flute, ...	"	$1 15	
Pressed ½ pint 6 Flute, ...	"	1 55	$1 67
Pressed ⅓ quart 6 Flute, ...	"		2 25
Pressed pint 6 Flute, ...	"		2 75
Pressed ⅓ quart Excelsior Footed, ...	"		2 40
Pressed ⅓ quart Excelsior Ship, ...	"		2 15
Pressed ½ pint Concave Flute, ...	"	2 10	2 25
Pressed ⅓ quart Mudge, ...	"		2 25
Pressed ½ pint Charleston, ...	"	1 85	2 00
Pressed ½ pint Lind, ...	"	1 25	
Pressed ⅓ quart Band Footed, ...	"		2 40
Pressed ⅓ quart Star, ...	"		2 25
Pressed ⅓ quart Gaines, ...	"		2 33
Pressed ½ pint Crystal, ...	"		2 00
Pressed ⅓ pint 9 Flute Light, ...	"	1 00	
Pressed ½ pint 9 Flute Light, ...	"	1 33	
Pressed ½ pint Eugenie Footed, ...	"		2 33
Pressed ½ pint Finger Flute, ...	"	1 45	1 55
Pressed ⅓ quart Finger Flute, ...	"		2 25
Pressed ½ pint Bigler Flute, ...	"	1 75	1 90
Pressed Temperance, ...	"		8 00
Pressed ½ pint Stedman, ...	"	1 67	1 80
Pressed ½ pint R. L.	"		1 87
Pressed ½ pint Mirror, ...	"		1 87
Pressed ½ pint 8 Flute, ...	"	1 33	
Pressed ½ pint Brilliant, ...	"		1 87
Pressed ½ pint Sprig, ...	"		1 87
Pressed Eureka Footed, ...	"		2 50

M'KEE & BROTHERS' PRICES OF GLASS WARE.

BAR TUMBLERS.

	Rough Bottoms.	Ground Bottoms.
Pressed gill 6 Flute Bar,..........per doz.	87	$1 00
Pressed gill New York Bar,.......... "	1 00	1 13
Pressed gill 6 Flute Jigger,.......... "	95	1 07
Pressed gill Crystal Bar,.......... "	1 00	1 13
Pressed gill Plain Bar,.......... "	95	1 07
Pressed ½ pint 6 Flute Foster Bar,.......... "		2 00
Pressed ⅓ pint Plain Bar,.......... "	1 50	1 65
Pressed ½ pint Plain Astor Bar,.......... "		2 33
Pressed ⅓ pint Plain Saloon Bar,.......... "	1 50	1 65
Pressed ⅛ pint Punch,.......... "		1 43
Pressed ⅓ quart Punch,.......... "		2 13
Pressed ½ pint 9 Flute Bar, extra heavy,.......... "		2 33
Pressed ⅓ pint New York Bar,.......... "	1 50	1 65
Pressed ½ pint New Orleans Bar,.......... "		1 80
Pressed ½ pint Gothic Bar,.......... "		2 00
Pressed ½ pint Gauche Bar,.......... "		2 00
Pressed ⅓ quart Gauche Bar,.......... "		2 25
Pressed ½ pint Mioton Bar,.......... "		2 25
Pressed ⅓ pint Crystal Bar,.......... "	1 50	1 65
Pressed ½ pint Hans Bar,.......... "		2 33
Pressed ⅓ pint Gauche Bar,.......... "		1 50
Pressed Minnie Bar,.......... "	95	1 07
Pressed ½ pint Lloyd Bar,.......... "		2 25
Pressed ½ pint " Cut Flutes,.......... "		3 60
Pressed ½ pint Plain Bar,.......... "		2 25
Pressed ½ pint Olive Bar,.......... "		2 00
Pressed ⅓ pint " .... "		1 65
Pressed 6 Flute Soda,.......... "		2 67

GOBLETS.
POLISHED FEET.

Pressed Excelsior,..........per doz.	$2 50
Pressed 6 Flute,.......... "	2 50
Pressed Crystal,.......... "	2 67
Pressed Mioten Hotel,.......... "	2 67
Pressed N. P. L.......... "	2 67
Pressed Prism,.......... "	2 67
Pressed Chain,.......... "	2 67
Pressed Sprig,.......... "	2 67
Pressed New York,.......... "	2 67
Pressed Eureka,.......... "	2 67
Pressed Leaf,.......... "	2 67

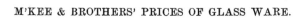

M'KEE & BROTHERS' PRICES OF GLASS WARE.

CHAMPAGNE GLASSES.

POLISHED FEET.

Pressed Excelsior,	per doz.	$2 00
Pressed 6 Flute,	"	2 00
Pressed Crystal,	"	2 15
Pressed N. P. L,	"	2 15
Pressed Prism,	"	2 15
Pressed Chain,	"	2 15
Pressed Sprig,	"	2 15
Pressed New York,	"	2 15
Pressed Mioton Hotel,	"	2 15
Pressed Eureka,	"	2 15

WINE GLASSES.

POLISHED FEET.

Pressed 6 Flute,	per doz.	$1 40
Pressed Excelsior,	"	1 40
Pressed Crystal,	"	1 50
Pressed Mioton Hotel,	"	1 50
Pressed N. P. L,	"	1 50
Pressed Prism,	"	1 50
Pressed Chain,	"	1 50
Pressed Sprig,	"	1 50
Pressed New York	"	1 50
Pressed Eureka,	"	1 50

ALE GLASSES.

Pressed Excelsior, or Long Tom,	per doz.	2 67
Pressed small pint 6 Flute,	"	2 60
Pressed Crystal,	"	2 50
Pressed Argus,	"	2 50
Pressed $\frac{1}{3}$ quart 10 Flute,	"	2 50
Pressed $\frac{1}{2}$ pint 10 Flute,	"	1 87
Pressed Poney 10 Flute,	"	1 67
Pressed $\frac{1}{2}$ pint Tyrrell, large,	"	2 33
Pressed $\frac{1}{2}$ pint Tyrrell, medium,	"	1 87
Pressed Poney Tyrrell,	"	1 67
Pressed New York,	"	2 67
Pressed Huber,	"	2 67
Pressed 6 Flute Knob,	"	2 13

M'KEE & BROTHERS' PRICES OF GLASS WARE.

BEER GLASSES.   Ground Bottoms.

Pressed B. V.,...	per doz.	$3 25
Pressed Cincinnati,...	"	3 00
Pressed Ohio	"	3 00
Pressed Crystal,...	"	3 00
Pressed 8 Flute,...	"	3 00
Pressed 8 Flute Poney,....................................	"	2 70
Pressed Argus,...	"	3 00
Pressed Argus Poney,......................................	"	2 50
Pressed Edge,..	"	3,25
Pressed Edge Poney,..	"	2 50
Pressed Sham,...	"	3 60
Pressed Sham Poney, ...	"	2 25
Pressed Crystal Poney,....................................	"	2 70

DECANTERS.

Pressed pint Excelsior and Patent Corks,...............	per doz.			$7 50
Pressed quart Excelsior,	"	"	"	9 50
Pressed pint Ring Bar,	"	"	"	4 25
Pressed quart Ring Bar,	"	"	"	5 50
Pressed pint Pillar,	"	"	"	11 25
Pressed quart Pillar,	"	"	"	13 50
Pressed quart Concave Flute,	"	"	"	10 00
Pressed quart Crystal,	"	"	"	11 25
Pressed quart R. L. Cut Neck,	"	"	"	15 00
Pressed quart R. L.,	"	"	"	11 25
Pressed quart Stedman,	"	"	"	11 25
Pressed quart Prism,	"	"	"	11 25
Quart Temperance,	"	"	each	2 50
Pressed Huber Glass Stopper............................	per doz.			13 25

JELLY GLASSES.

Pressed Excelsior,..	per doz.	$2 00
Pressed 6 Flute Jelly Cups, Footed,.....................	"	1 75
Pressed ½ pint 10 Flute Jelly Tumblers,................	"	1 25
Pressed ½ pint 10 Flute Jelly Tumblers,................	"	1 60
Pressed ½ pint Plain Jelly Tumblers,....................	"	1 00
Pressed ⅓ pint Plain Jelly, "	"	80

M'KEE & BROTHERS' PRICES OF GLASS WARE.

BITTER BOTTLES.

Pressed 6 Flute,...per doz. $4 50
Pressed 8 Flute,... "   3 50
Pressed Excelsior,.. "   5 00
Pressed Stedman,... "   4 50

WATER BOTTLES.

Pint Plain,...per doz. $5 00
Quart Plain, ... "   6 00

LIQUORS AND CORDIALS.
POLISHED FEET.

Pressed Mioton Hotel,..................................per doz. $1 25
Pressed Eureka,.. "   1 25

PRESSED PLATES.

3 inch Diamond,...per doz. $ 36
6 inch Ray,... "   1 25
6 inch R. L... "   1 25
6 inch Stedman,... "   1 25
6 inch Sprig,... "   1 25

PRESSED CASTER BOTTLES.

Swell Flute, Screw Top,...........................per doz. $1 00
No. 17,   "   .... "   1 00
Eugenie,   "   .... "   1 10
Gaines,   Brit. Top, ... "   2 13
Cincinnati,   "   "   .... "   2 13
Large Saloon Peppers, ... "   2 13

M'KEE & BROTHERS' PRICES OF GLASS WARE.

MOLASSES CANS.

Pint Pillar, Metal Tops,..per doz.	$9 50	
Excelsior, Metal Tops,..........................	"	5 25
Excelsior, Tin Tops,..	"	4 00
No. 14, Metal Tops,...	"	5 25
No. 14, Tin Tops,........................	"	4 00
Rose, Metal Tops,..	"	6 00
Rose, Tin Tops,.......................................	"	4 75
Pint Fine Ribbed, Glass stoppers,.........	"	2 50
Diamond, Tin Tops,.......	"	4 25
Diamond, Metal Tops,...	"	5 50
R. L., Metal Tops,.......	"	5 50
R. L., Tin Tops,.. ..	"	4 25
Stedman, Metal Tops,...............	"	5 50
Stedman, Tin Tops,.........	"	4 25
Morton, Tin Tops,..	"	4 25
Morton, Brit. Tops,..................	"	5 50

CARBON OIL LAMPS.

Ring Hand,........... ....per doz.	$4 00	
Ring Footed,.....	"	5 00
Ribbed Footed,............................	"	5 00
Ribbed Hand,......	"	4 00
Argus Footed,...	"	5 50
Concave Footed,......	"	5 50
R. L. Footed,.....	"	5 50
Shell Footed,..............................	"	6 50
Sprig Footed,...	"	6 50
Tulip Footed, ...	"	6 50
Vine Footed,..	"	6 50
Stedman Footed,......	"	6 50
Prism Footed, ...	"	6 50
Ring, 4 inch Colored Base,...........	"	7 00
Ribbed, 4 inch Colored Base,.....................................	"	7 00
Turnip, 4 inch Colored Base,......................................	"	7 00
R. L., 4 inch Colored Base,...	"	7 00
Argus, 4 inch Colored Base,..	"	7 00
Concave, 4 inch Colored Base,.....................................	"	7 00
Shell, 5 inch Colored Base,...	"	9 00
Sprig, 5 inch Colored Base,...	"	9 00
Tulip, 5 inch Colored Base,...	"	9 00
Vine, 5 inch Colored Base,..	"	9 00

M'KEE & BROTHERS' PRICES OF GLASS WARE.

CARBON OIL LAMPS.

Ellipse, 5 inch Colored Base,......................................per doz.		9 00
Star and Concave, 5 inch Colored Base,........................	"	9 00
Chain, 5 inch Colored Base,.......................................	"	9 00
Gaines, 5 inch Colored Base,......................................	"	9 00
Prism, 5 inch Colored Base,..	"	9 00
Cincinnati, 5 inch Colored Base,.................................	"	9 00
Stedman, 5 inch Colored Base,....................................	"	9 00
Large Suspension Fountain, No. 1 Burners....................	"	5 50
Small Suspension Fountain, No. 1 Burners,....................	"	5 00
Large Suspension Fountain, No. 2 Burners,....................	"	9 50
Large Harps for Hanging Lamps, Bronzed,....................	"	3 50
Small Harps for Hanging Lamps, Bronzed,....................	"	3 50
Small Side Brackets and Reflecters,.............................	"	5 00
Large Side Brackets and Reflecters,.............................	"	5 00
Pressed Assorted Large Pegs, Ellipse, Star, Concave, Chain, Gaines, Cincinnati, Shell, Prism, Sted- man, Tulip, Sprig, Vine,.......................................}	per doz.	$2 20
Assorted Small Pegs, R. L. Concave and Argus,............	"	1 60
Assorted Small Pegs, Ribbed and Ring..........................	"	1 50
Pressed R. L. Footed Lamps, no Burner,.......................	"	3 50
Pressed Argus Footed Lamps, no Burner.......................	"	3 50
Pressed Concave Footed Lamps, no Burner, ...	"	3 50
Pressed Ring Footed Lamps, no Burner, ...	"	3 00
Pressed Ribbed Footed Lamps, no Burner, ...	"	3 00
Pressed Large Suspension Fount, No. 1 or No. 2 Mouths,.	"	3 50
Pressed Small Suspension Fount, No. 1 Mouth,..............	"	2 40
3½ inch White Base and Stem,.....................................	"	3 50
3½ Black Base and Stem,..	"	3 00
Pressed 4 inch White Base and Stem, ...	"	4 00
Pressed 4 inch Black Base and Stem,...........................	"	3 75
Pressed 5 inch White Base and Stem.	"	5 50
Pressed 5 inch Black Base and Stem............................	"	5 00
Pressed Ring Hand Lamp, no Burner,............................	"	2 20
Pressed Ribbed Hand Lamp, no Burner,........................	"	2 20

BACON'S BURNERS (for burning without Chimneys), will be substituted at the same price when desired.

M'KEE & BROTHERS' PRICES OF GLASS WARE.

CANDLESTICKS.

Pressed French, no Sockets, ...per doz.	$3	50
Pressed Boston, with Sockets,.. "	7	25
Pressed Dolphin, with Sockets,.................................... "	6	25
Pressed 6 Flute, no Sockets, ... "	4	25

CELERY GLASSES.

Pressed Ray,...per doz.	$8	00
Pressed Eugenie,.. "	6	25
Pressed Crystal,... "	8	50
Pressed Sprig, ... "	8	50

PRESSED DISHES.

6 inch Shell,..per doz.	$2	00
7 inch Shell,.. "	2	70
8 inch Shell,.. "	4	00
7 inch Oval Star, ... "	2	50
8 inch Oval Mitre,... "	3	25
Shell Pickle,.. "	2	00
7 inch Ray,.. "	2	75
9 inch Ray,.. "	5	00
7 inch Eugenie Dish, on Foot, and Cover, ... "	7	50
9 inch Eugenie Dish, on Foot, and Cover, ... "	12	00
8 inch Crystal Dish, on Foot, and Cover,........................ "	10	00
Shell Sauce, ... "	4	50
7 inch N. P. L.. "	2	33
8 inch N. P. L.. "	3	50
9 inch N. P. L.. "	4	50
7 inch Sprig, ... "	2	33
8 inch Sprig, ... "	3	50
9 inch Sprig, ... "	4	50
7 inch Eureka,.. "	2	33
8 inch Eureka,.. "	3	50
9 inch Eureka,.. "	4	50

M'KEE & BROTHERS' PRICES OF GLASS WARE.

LANTERNS.—Spring Bottoms.

Cone Flute, Oil or Candle,	per doz.	$7 00
No. 2 Pear, Oil or Candle,	"	7 50
No. 3 Pear, Oil or Candle,	"	8 00
Cone Flute, Oil or Candle, Guarded,	"	8 50
No. 2 Pear, Oil or Candle, Guarded,	"	9 00
No. 3 Pear, Oil or Candle, Guarded,	"	9 50
6 inch Globe, Oil or Candle, Guarded,	"	9 00
8 inch Globe, Oil or Candle, Guarded	"	16 50

CARBON OIL LANTERNS.—Spring Bottoms.

No. 2 Pear, Guarded,	per doz.	$12 00
No. 3 Pear, Guarded,	"	12 50
6 inch Globe, Guarded,	"	12 00

BOWLS FOR HOTELS AND COFFEE HOUSES.

8 inch Cracker, Tin Covers,	per doz.	$20 00
10 inch Cracker, Tin Covers,	"	25 00
8 inch Cracker, Tin Covers, Low Foot,	"	18 00

SYRUP CANS AND BOTTLES.

Pint Pillar Syrup Cans,	per doz.	$6 50
Pint Pillar Syrup Bottles,	"	5 00
Pint Fluted Syrup Cans,	"	5 00
Pint Fluted Syrup Bottles,	"	3 60
Pint Plain Syrup Cans,	"	5 50
Heavy Plain Syrup Bottles,	"	8 00

LAMP CHIMNEYS.

	Flint.		Lime.
No. 0 Coal Oil, Net,	per doz. $ 70	per doz. $	45
No. 1 Coal Oil, "	" 80	"	45
No. 2 Coal Oil, "	" 1 10	"	65
No. 3 Coal Oil, "	" 1 65	"	1 00
No. 1 Nut Crackers,	" 1 10		
No. 1 Sun,	" 1 10	"	60

M'KEE & BROTHERS' PRICES OF GLASS WARE.

SPOON HOLDERS.—Polished Feet.

Pressed Crystal,..per doz.	$3	00
Pressed N. P. L.. "	3	00
Pressed Sprig,,.. "	3	00
Pressed Eureka,.. "	3	00

EGG GLASSES.—Polished Feet.

Pressed Excelsior,...per doz.	$1	60
Pressed Crystal,.. "	1	60
Pressed N. P. L.. "	1	67
Pressed Sprig,.. "	1	67
Pressed New York,... "	1	67
Pressed Eureka, ... "	1	67

SWEETMEATS.—Footed, with Covers.

Pressed 6 inch Crystal and Covers,...............................per doz.	$6	25
Pressed 6 inch Sprig and Covers,................................. "	6	25
Pressed 6 inch Eureka and Covers, ... "	6	25
Pressed 6 inch N. P. L. and Covers,............................. "	6	25

PRESSED SAUCERS AND NAPPIES.

7 inch Ray Nappies,..per doz.	$2	87
6 inch Ray Nappies,... "	1	75
5 inch Ray Nappies,... "	1	25
4 inch Ray Nappies,... "		75
6 inch Crystal Nappies,.. "	2	33
6 inch Crystal Nappies and Covers, ... "	4	67
5 inch N. P. L. Nappies,... "	1	25
6 inch N. P. L. Nappies,... "	2	25
6 inch N. P. L. Nappies and Covers,............................. "	4	50
4 inch N. P. L. Nappies.. "		70
6 inch Sprig Nappies and Covers,................................. "	4	50
6 inch Sprig Nappies, ... "	2	25
4 inch Sprig Nappies, ... "		70
6 inch Eureka Nappies,.. "	2	25
6 inch Eureka Nappies and Covers,............................... "	4	50
4 inch Eureka Nappies,.. "		70
5 inch Eureka Nappies,.. "	1	25

M'KEE & BROTHERS' PRICES OF GLASS WARE.

PRESSED SALTS.

Pressed Concave,	per doz. $		67
Pressed Fillmore,	"	1	67
Pressed Mason,	"	1	67
Pressed Rope,	"	2	13
Pressed Imperial,	"	2	13
Pressed Tomato,	"	2	50
Pressed Diamond Individual,	"		55
Pressed Tulip,	"		95
Pressed Lotus,	"	2	00
Pressed Diamond,	"	1	25
Pressed Round Individual,	"		55
Pressed N. P. L.	"	1	25
Pressed Stedman,	"	1	75
Pressed Cincinnati, Individual,	"		55
Pressed Sprig,	"	1	25
Pressed Eureka,	"	1	25

SUGAR BOWLS AND COVERS.

Pressed Band,	per doz. $4		50
Pressed Ray,	"	7	00
Pressed Crystal,	"	6	00
Pressed N. P. L.	"	6	25
Pressed Sprig,	"	6	00
Pressed Eureka,	"	6	25

PRESSED BOWLS.

9 inch Concave Bowls,	per doz. $11		00
10 inch Excelsior Bowls,	"	15	00
10 inch Scollop Diamond Bowls,	"	16	50
8 inch Crystal Bowls,	"	10	00
10 inch Crystal Bowls,	"	16	50
10 inch Leaf Bowls,	"	15	50
7 inch N. P. L. Bowls, low foot,	"	7	00
7 inch N. P. L. Bowls, low foot and Covers,	"	12	00
7 inch N. P. L. Bowls, high foot,	"	8	33
7 inch N. P. L. Bowls, high foot and Covers,	"	13	33
8 inch N. P. L. Bowls, low foot,	"	8	00
8 inch N. P. L. Bowls, low foot and Covers,	"	14	00
8 inch N. P. L. Bowls, high foot,	"	9	33
8 inch N. P. L. Bowls, high foot and Covers,	"	15	33
8 inch Sprig Bowls, low foot,	"	8	00
8 inch Sprig Bowls, high foot,	"	9	33

M'KEE & BROTHERS' PRICES OF GLASS WARE.

PRESSED BOWLS

10 inch Sprig Bowls, high foot,	"	18 00
7 inch Sprig Bowls, high foot,	"	8 33
7 inch Sprig Bowls, low foot,	"	7 00
7 inch Eureka Bowls, low foot,	"	7 00
7 inch Eureka Bowls, low foot and Covers,	"	12 00
7 inch Eureka Bowls, high foot,	"	8 33
7 inch Eureka Bowls, high foot and Covers,	"	13 33
8 inch Eureka Bowls, high foot,	"	9 33
8 inch Eureka Bowls, high foot and Covers,	"	15 33
8 inch Eureka Bowls, low foot,	"	8 00
8 inch Eureka Bowls, low foot and Covers,	"	14 00

PITCHERS AND CREAMS.

Pressed large quart Excelsior,	per doz. $	8 00
Pressed large pint Excelsior,	"	7 50
Pressed large quart Concave,	"	9 00
Pressed ½ pint Plain Creams,	"	2 67
Pressed quart Crystal Pitchers,	"	11 00
Pressed ⅓ quart Crystal Creams,	"	4 75
Pressed ½ gallon R. L. Pitchers,	"	15 00
Pressed ⅓ quart N. P. L. Creams,	"	4 75
Pressed ½ gallon N. P. L. Pitchers,	"	15 00
Pressed quart Prism Pitchers,	"	11 00
Pressed ½ gallon Prism Pitchers,	"	15 00
Pressed ⅓ quart Sprig Creams,	"	4 75
Pressed ½ gallon Sprig Pitchers,	"	15 00
Pressed ⅓ quart Eureka Creams,	"	4 75
Pressed ½ gallon Eureka Pitchers,	"	15 00

SALVERS AND CAKE COVERS.

Plain 6 inches,	each, $	60
Plain 7 inches,	"	67
Plain 8 inches,	"	75
Plain 9 inches,	"	1 00
Plain 10 inches,	"	1 25
Plain 11 inches,	"	1 60
Plain 12 inches,	"	1 75
Plain 13 inches,	"	2 00
Plain 14 inches,	"	2 25
Plain 15 inches,	"	3 00

M'KEE & BROTHERS' PRICES OF GLASS WARE.

SUNDRIES.

Toys,	per gross,	$4 75
Bird Fountains,	per doz.	2 33
Seed Boxes,	"	1 75
Julep Tubes,	"	30
Fish Globes made to order,	each, from 75 cts. up to	8 00
Shoemakers' Globes,	per doz.	2 33
Bird Baths,	"	1 75
Butter Prints,	"	3 00
White Enameled Glass Eggs,	"	1 25
Plain Altar Cruets,	"	15 00
Engraved Altar Cruets,	"	20 00
Well Inkstands,	"	5 00
Soap Slabs,	"	2 00
Night Lamps, for Fluid,	"	2 00
Hyacinth Glasses,	"	3 00

APOTHECARIES'
SHOP FURNITURE,
MADE OF FLINT GLASS.

Specie Jars, with Tin Japanned Covers.

3 gallon,	per doz. $19 50		½ gallon,	per doz. $4 50	
2 gallon,	"	12 38	1 quart,	"	3 38
6 quart,	"	9 50	1 pint,	"	2 25
1 gallon,	"	6 75	½ pint,	"	1 75
3 quart,	"	5 75			

Specie Jars, with Tin Japanned Covers.
SQUAT SHAPE.

2 gallon,	per doz. $12 75		1 quart,	per doz. $3 50	
1 gallon,	"	7 00	1 pint,	"	2 38
3 quart,	"	6 00	½ pint,	"	1 83
½ gallon,	"	4 63			

M'KEE & BROTHERS' PRICES OF GLASS WARE.

Two Ring Jars, with Glass Covers.

2 gallon,	............per doz.	$27 00	3 quart,	..............per doz.	$15 00
6 quart,	.... "	22 50	½ gallon,	.... "	12 50
1 gallon,	.... "	18 00	1 quart,	.... "	8 50
Confectionary Jars made to order.			Large Show Jars made to order.		

Tinctures, with Ground Mushroom Stoppers.

2 gallon,	............per doz.	$13 50	1 quart,	..............per doz.	$4 00
6 quart,	.... "	11 75	1 pint,	.... "	2 75
1 gallon,	.... "	8 25	½ pint and 4 oz	...... "	2 25
½ gallon,	.... "	6 00	1 and 2 oz	.... "	1 80

Salt Mouths, with Ground Mushroom Stoppers.

2 gallon,	............per doz.	$15 00	1 quart,	..............per doz.	$5 00
6 quart,	.... "	13 50	1 pint,	.... "	3 60
1 gallon,	.... "	10 25	½ pint and 4 oz	...... "	2 50
½ gallon,	.... "	6 75	1 and 2 oz	.... "	2 25

Graduates.

Minimum,	....per doz.	$ 6 00
1 oz	.... "	5 40
2 oz	.... "	6 00
3 oz	.... "	6 60
4 oz	.... "	8 00
6 oz	.... "	8 40
8 oz	.... "	10 80
12 oz	.... "	14 40
16 oz	.... "	18 00
32 oz	.... "	30 00

Mortars and Pestles.

Gill,	....per doz.	$11 00
½ pint,	.... "	12 00
Pint,	.... "	18 00
Quart,	.... "	23 00
½ gallon,	.... "	36 00

Funnels.

Gill,	....per doz.	$ 1 80
½ pint,	.... "	2 25
Pint,	.... "	2 50
Quart,	.... "	3 60
½ gallon,	.... "	6 25
Assorted,	.... "	3 60

M'KEE & BROTHERS' PRICES OF GLASS WARE.

Syringes.

Pocket,	per doz. $	1 20
1 oz. Male, Capped,	"	1 25
2 oz. Male, Capped,	"	1 50
3 oz. Male, Capped,	"	1 75
1 oz. Female, Capped,	"	1 50
2 oz. Female, Capped,	"	1 75
3 oz. Female, Capp d,	"	2 00
4 oz. Female, Capped,	"	2 50
Curved Womb,	"	4 00
Straight Womb,	"	4 00
Ear,	"	1 75
Eye,	"	1 50

Show Globes.

½ gallon, 2 pieces, Cone or Globe shape,	each, $	1 50
1 gallon, 2 pieces, Cone or Globe shape,	"	1 80
2 gallon, 2 pieces, Cone or Globe shape,	"	3 00
3 gallon, 3 pieces, Cone or Globe shape,	"	4 50
1 gallon, 3 pieces, Pear shape,	"	2 50
2 gallon, 3 pieces, Pear shape,	"	3 60
3 gallon, 3 pieces, Pear shape,	"	5 50
5 gallon, 4 pieces, French Style,	"	12 00
5 gallon, 3 pieces, French Style, engraved, net,	"	18 00
3 gallon, 3 pieces, French Style,	"	7 25

Miscellaneous.

Breast Pipes,	per doz.	$3 75
Nipple Shells,	"	1 70
Nursing Bottles,	"	3 75
Nipple Shields,	"	2 75
Flat Pessaries,	"	2 25
Globe Pessaries,	"	3 00
½, 1 and 2 oz. Cupping Glasses,	"	1 50
Nested Cupping Glasses,	"	2 25
4 oz. Cupping Glasses,	"	2 25
8 oz. Cupping Glasses,	"	3 00
Glass Speculums,	"	4 75
Male and Female Urinals,	"	5 75
¼, ½, 1 and 2 drachm Flint Vials,	per gro.	2 00
Glass Inhalers,	per doz.	5 50
Glass Spittoons,	"	3 75
Vaccine Glasses,	"	4 50
Eye Glasses,	"	3 00
Proof Vials,	"	2 00

M'KEE & BROTHERS' PRICES OF GLASS WARE.

Receivers and Retorts.

Plain pint, ...each, $	55	Tubulated pint, ...each, $	80
" quart, ... "	80	" quart, ... "	1 25
" ½ gallon, ... "	1 25	" ½ gallon, ... "	2 00
" gallon, ... "	1 65	" gallon, ... "	2 80

☞ **Glass Tubing, Cane, Spirit Lamps, Electrical Cylinders, Retorts, Receivers, Florence Flasks, together with Chemical and Philosophical Apparatus, all made to order.**

GLASS LABELS.
Put on Furniture to order.
[NET PRICES.]

Square Labels, Black and Gold.

1 gallon, ...each, $	40
½ gallon, ... "	30
Quart and under, ... "	25
Fancy Colors, each, extra, ...	5

Shields or Ovals (in any Style).

1 gallon, ...each, $	50
½ gallon, ... "	40
Quart and under, ... "	30

TERMS.

All Bills NET CASH, less............per cent. Discount, to be paid within TEN days from date of Invoice.

☞ With the latest improvements and superior facilities for manufacturing, we can assure our customers that there is nothing elegant or extra in Flint Glass Ware, made or furnished in this vicinity, but we make and supply.

As we have our Glass put up by experienced packers, in the most neat and careful manner, WE MAKE NO ALLOWANCE FOR BREAKAGE—Bills of Lading being guarantee of good order when shipped.

Do you wish to have your Goods Insured?

We have an open Policy, covering shipments to all points, at as low rates as can be secured here, and include the premium in your merchandise account.   Please say INSURE, in all cases where you want the goods covered by us.

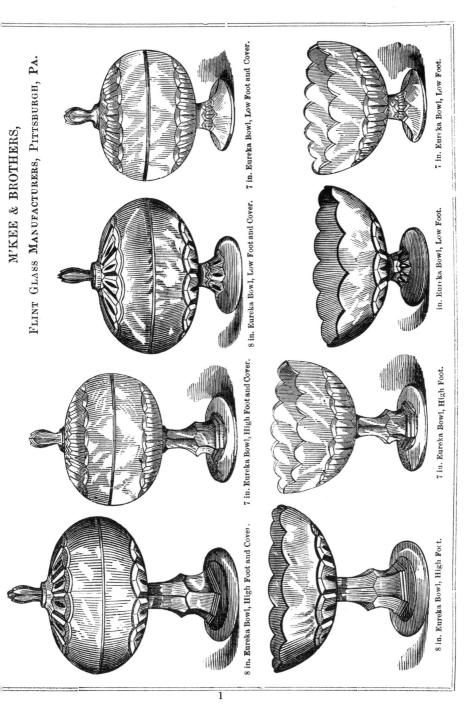

M'KEE & BROTHERS,

FLINT GLASS MANUFACTURERS, PITTSBURGH, PA.

7 in. Eureka Bowl, Low Foot and Cover.

8 in. Eureka Bowl, Low Foot and Cover.

7 in. Eureka Bowl, High Foot and Cover.

8 in. Eureka Bowl, High Foot and Cover.

7 in. Eureka Bowl, Low Foot.

in. Eureka Bowl, Low Foot.

7 in. Eureka Bowl, High Foot.

8 in. Eureka Bowl, High Foot.

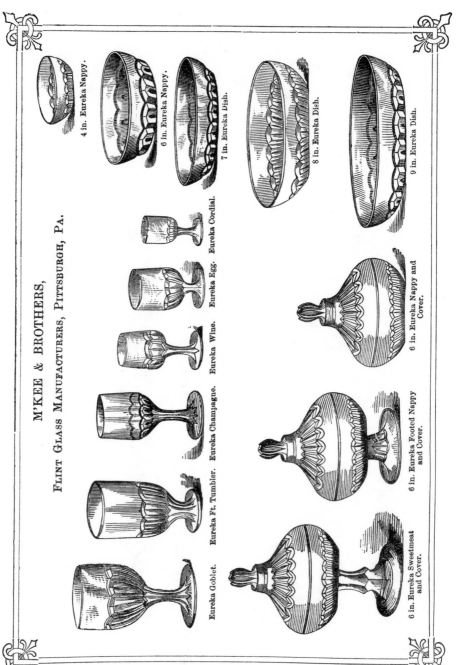

M'KEE & BROTHERS,

FLINT GLASS MANUFACTURERS, PITTSBURGH, PA.

4 in. Eureka Nappy.

6 in. Eureka Nappy.

7 in. Eureka Dish.

8 in. Eureka Dish.

9 in. Eureka Dish.

Eureka Cordial.

Eureka Egg.

Eureka Wine.

Eureka Champagne.

Eureka Ft. Tumbler.

Eureka Goblet.

6 in. Eureka Nappy and Cover.

6 in. Eureka Footed Nappy and Cover.

6 in. Eureka Sweetmeat and Cover.

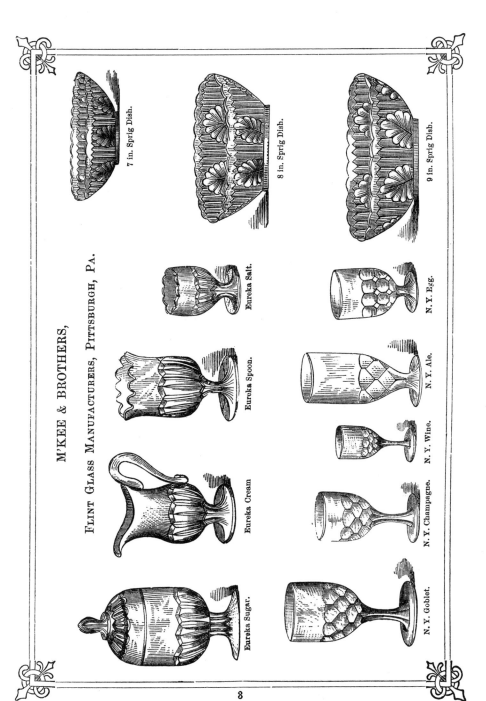

M'KEE & BROTHERS,

FLINT GLASS MANUFACTURERS, PITTSBURGH, PA.

7 in. Sprig Dish.

8 in. Sprig Dish.

9 in. Sprig Dish.

Eureka Salt.

N. Y. Egg.

Eureka Spoon.

N. Y. Ale.

N. Y. Wine.

Eureka Cream

N. Y. Champagne.

Eureka Sugar.

N. Y. Goblet.

M'KEE & BROTHERS,

FLINT GLASS MANUFACTURERS, PITTSBURGH, PA.

6 in. Sprig Nappy and Cover.

6 in. Sprig Sweetmeat and Cover.

6 in. Sprig Nappy

4 in. Sprig Nappy.

7 in. Sprig Bowl, Low Foot.

6 in. Sprig Plate.

8 in. Sprig Bowl, High Foot.

8 in. Sprig Bowl, Low Foot.

½ gall. Sprig Pitcher.

M'KEE & BROTHERS, FLINT GLASS MANUFACTURERS, PITTSBURGH, PA.

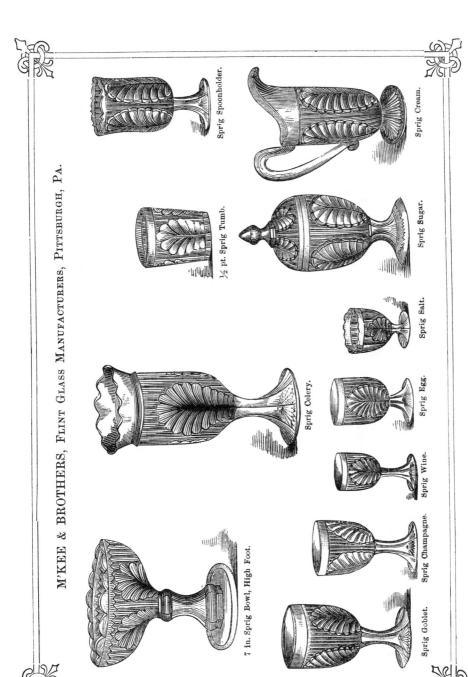

Sprig Spoonholder.

Sprig Cream.

½ pt. Sprig Tumb.

Sprig Sugar.

Sprig Salt.

Sprig Celery.

Sprig Egg.

Sprig Wine.

7 in. Sprig Bowl, High Foot.

Sprig Champagne.

Sprig Goblet.

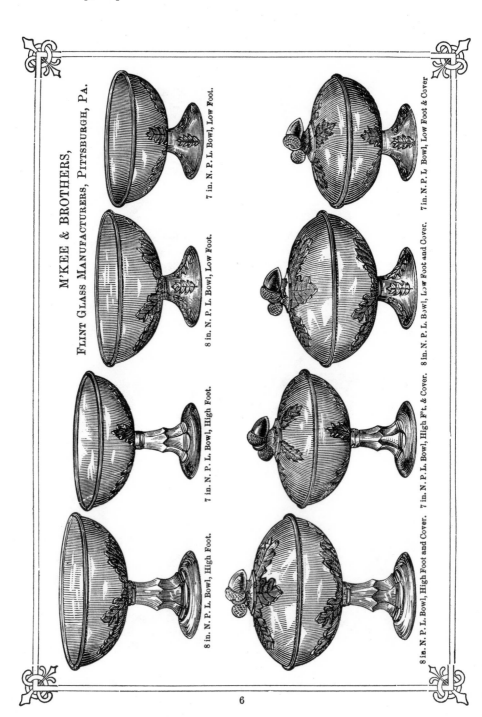

M'KEE & BROTHERS,
FLINT GLASS MANUFACTURERS, PITTSBURGH, PA.

7 in. N. P. L. Bowl, Low Foot.

8 in. N. P. L. Bowl, Low Foot.

7 in. N. P. L. Bowl, High Foot.

8 in. N. P. L. Bowl, High Foot.

7 in. N. P. L. Bowl, Low Foot & Cover.

8 in. N. P. L. Bowl, Low Foot and Cover.

7 in. N. P. L. Bowl, High F't, & Cover.

8 in. N. P. L. Bowl, High Foot and Cover.

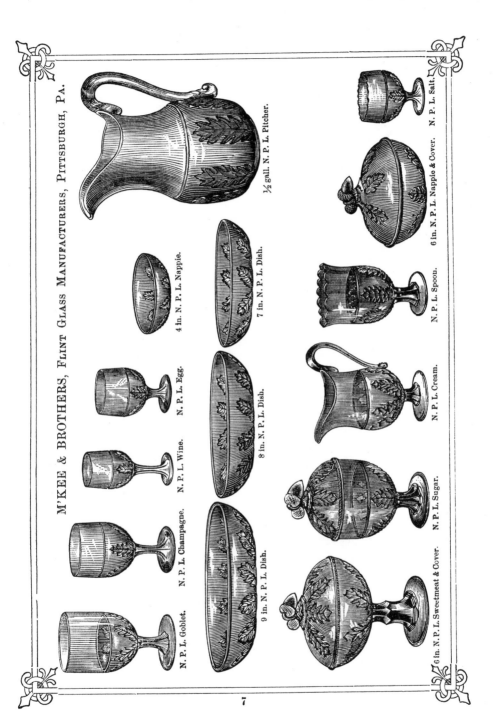

M'KEE & BROTHERS, FLINT GLASS MANUFACTURERS, PITTSBURGH, PA.

½ gall. N. P. L. Pitcher.

4 in. N. P. L. Nappie.

7 in. N. P. L. Dish.

N. P. L. Egg.

N. P. L. Wine.

8 in. N. P. L. Dish.

N. P. L. Champagne.

N. P. L. Goblet.

9 in. N. P. L. Dish.

N. P. L. Salt.

6 in. N. P. L. Nappie & Cover.

N. P. L. Spoon.

N. P. L. Cream.

N. P. L. Sugar.

6 in. N. P. L. Sweetmeat & Cover.

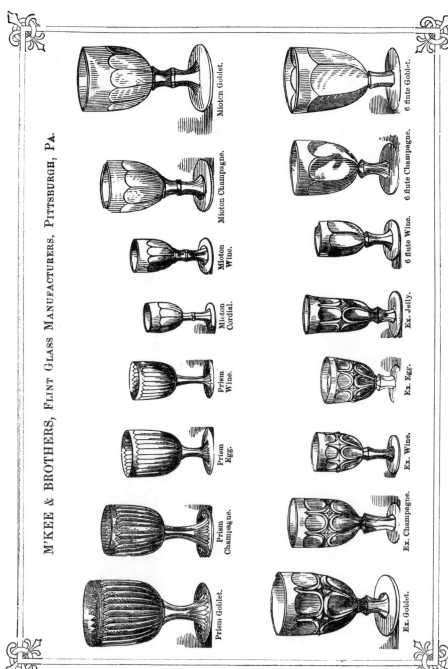

M'KEE & BROTHERS, FLINT GLASS MANUFACTURERS, PITTSBURGH, PA.

Mioton Goblet.

Mioton Champagne.

Mioton Wine.

Mioton Cordial.

Prism Wine.

Prism Egg.

Prism Champagne.

Prism Goblet.

6 flute Goblet.

6 flute Champagne.

6 flute Wine.

Ex. Jelly.

Ex. Egg.

Ex. Wine.

Ex. Champagne.

Ex. Goblet.

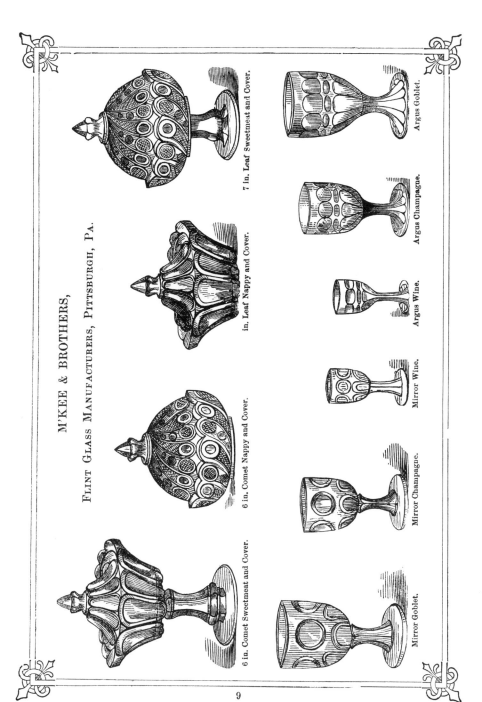

M'KEE & BROTHERS,

FLINT GLASS MANUFACTURERS, PITTSBURGH, PA.

7 in. Leaf Sweetmeat and Cover.

in. Leaf Nappy and Cover.

6 in. Comet Nappy and Cover.

6 in. Comet Sweetmeat and Cover.

Argus Goblet.

Argus Champagne.

Argus Wine.

Mirror Wine.

Mirror Champagne.

Mirror Goblet.

9

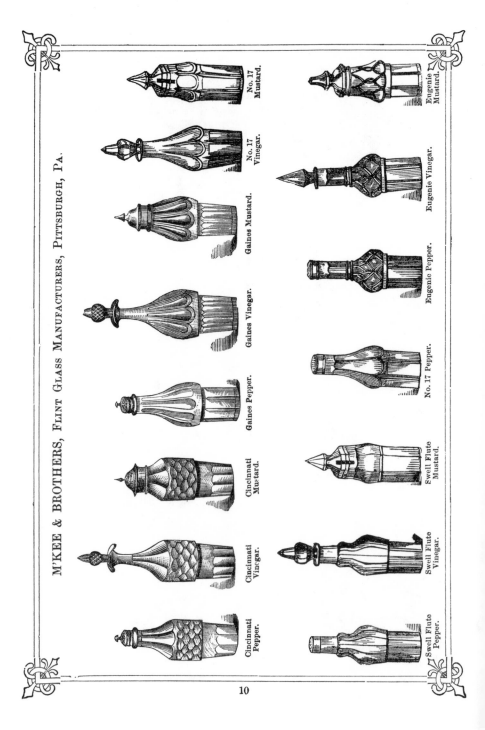

M'KEE & BROTHERS, FLINT GLASS MANUFACTURERS, PITTSBURGH, PA.

No. 17 Mustard.

No. 17 Vinegar.

Gaines Mustard.

Gaines Vinegar.

Gaines Pepper.

Cincinnati Mustard.

Cincinnati Vinegar.

Cincinnati Pepper.

Eugenie Mustard.

Eugenie Vinegar.

Eugenie Pepper.

No. 17 Pepper.

Swell Flute Mustard.

Swell Flute Vinegar.

Swell Flute Pepper.

M'KEE & BROTHERS,

FLINT GLASS MANUFACTURERS, PITTSBURGH, PA.

Pt. Pillared Decanter.

Bird Fountain.

Feed Box.

Ring Decanter.

6 in. Shell Dish.

Qt. R. L. Decanter.

7 in. Shell Dish.

Qt. Stedman Decanter.

8 in. Shell Dish.

Qt Pillared Decanter.

11

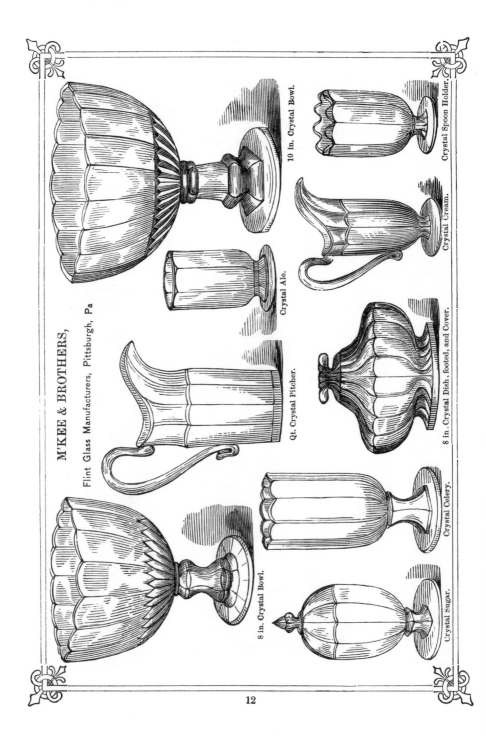

M'KEE & BROTHERS,

Flint Glass Manufacturers, Pittsburgh, Pa

10 in. Crystal Bowl.

Crystal Spoon Holder.

Crystal Cream.

Crystal Ale.

Qt. Crystal Pitcher.

8 in. Crystal Dish, footed, and Cover.

Crystal Celery.

8 in. Crystal Bowl.

Crystal Sugar.

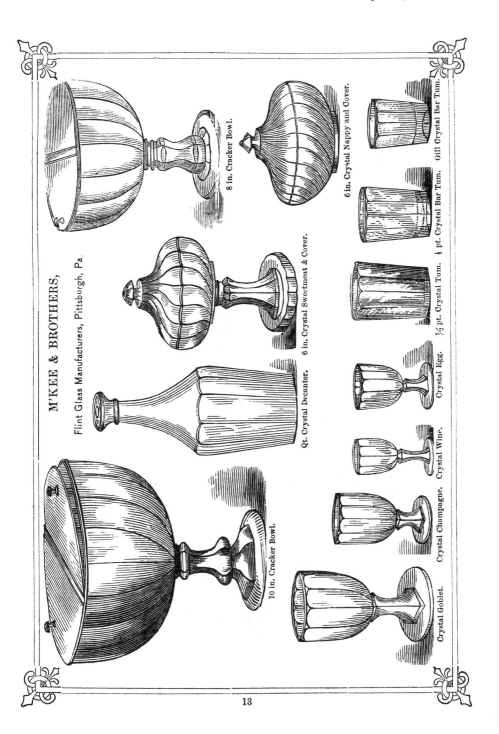

M'KEE & BROTHERS,

Flint Glass Manufacturers, Pittsburgh, Pa.

8 in. Cracker Bowl.

6 in. Crystal Nappy and Cover.

Gill Crystal Bar Tum.

½ pt. Crystal Bar Tum.

½ pt. Crystal Tum.

6 in. Crystal Sweetmeat & Cover.

Qt. Crystal Decanter.

½ pt. Crystal Tum.

Crystal Egg.

Crystal Wine.

10 in. Cracker Bowl.

Crystal Champagne.

Crystal Goblet.

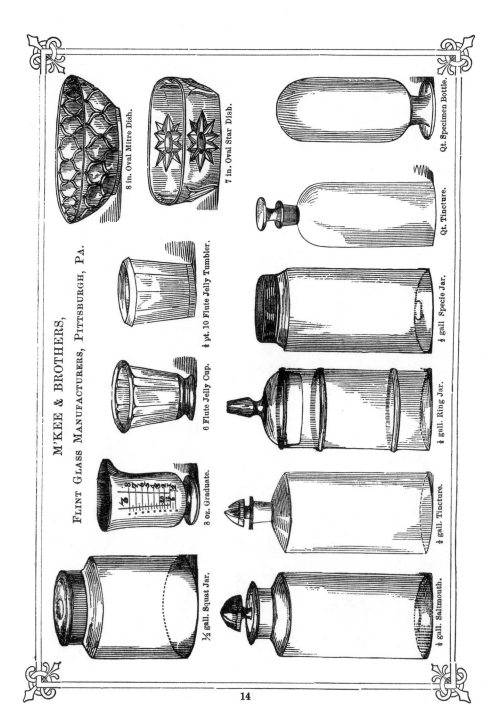

M'KEE & BROTHERS,
FLINT GLASS MANUFACTURERS, PITTSBURGH, PA.

8 in. Oval Mitre Dish.

7 in. Oval Star Dish.

Qt. Specimen Bottle.

Qt. Tincture.

½ pt. 10 Flute Jelly Tumbler.

6 Flute Jelly Cup.

½ gall Specie Jar.

¼ gall. Ring Jar.

8 oz. Graduate.

¼ gall. Tincture.

½ gall. Squat Jar.

¼ gall. Saltmouth.

M'KEE & BROTHERS,

FLINT GLASS MANUFACTURERS, PITTSBURGH, PA.

Pt. Ex. Decanter.

Pt. Ex. Pitcher.

Ex. Ale.

Ex. Bitter.

⅓ qt. Ex. foot Tumb.

½ qt. Ex. Ship Tumb.

10 in. Ex. Bowl.

Qt. Ex. Decanter.

Qt. Ex. Pitcher.

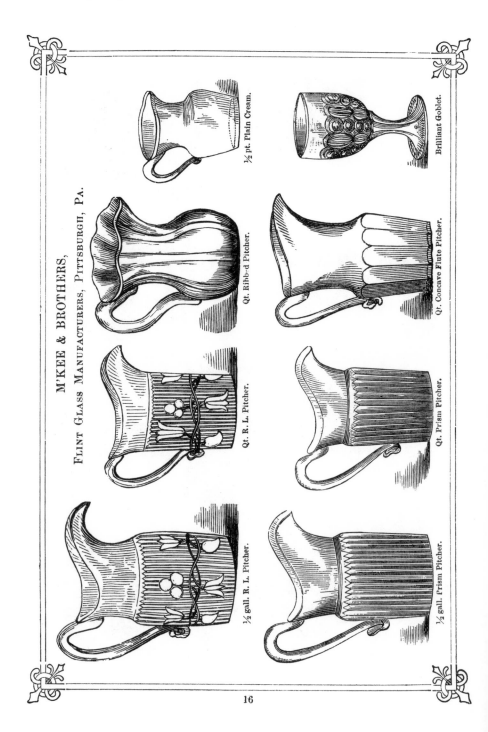

M'KEE & BROTHERS,
FLINT GLASS MANUFACTURERS, PITTSBURGH, PA.

½ pt. Plain Cream.

Brilliant Goblet.

Qt. Ribb-d Pitcher.

Qt. Concave Flute Pitcher.

Qt. R. L. Pitcher.

Qt. Prism Pitcher.

½ gall. R. L. Pitcher.

½ gall. Prism Pitcher.

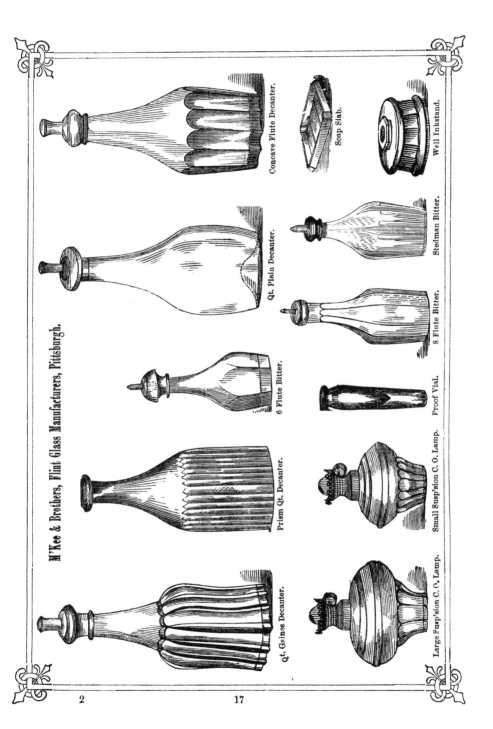

M'Kee & Brothers, Flint Glass Manufacturers, Pittsburgh.

Concave Flute Decanter.

Soap Slab.

Well Inkstand.

Qt. Plain Decanter.

Stedman Bitter.

8 Flute Bitter.

6 Flute Bitter.

Proof Vial.

Prism Qt. Decanter.

Small Susp'sion C. O. Lamp.

Qt. Gaines Decanter.

Large Susp'sion C. O. Lamp.

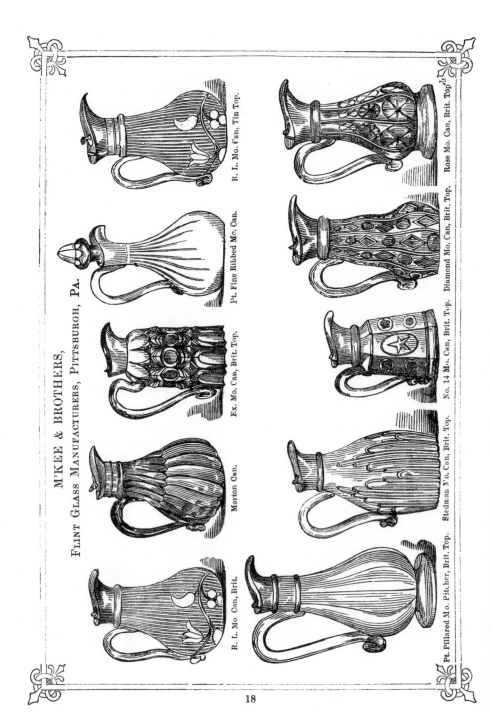

M'KEE & BROTHERS,
FLINT GLASS MANUFACTURERS, PITTSBURGH, PA.

R. L. Mo. Can, Tin Top.

Pt. Fine Ribbed Mo. Can.

Ex. Mo. Can, Brit. Top.

Morton Can.

R. L. Mo Can, Brit.

Rose Mo. Can, Brit. Top.

Diamond Mo. Can, Brit. Top.

No. 14 Mo. Can, Brit. Top.

Stedman No. Can, Brit. Top.

Pt. Pillared Mo. Pitcher, Brit. Top.

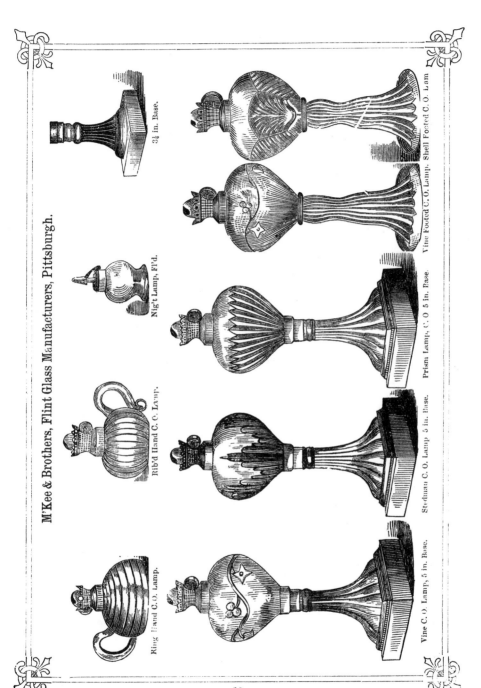

M'Kee & Brothers, Flint Glass Manufacturers, Pittsburgh.

3¼ in. Base.

Nig't Lamp, Fl'd.

Rib'd Hand C. O. Lamp.

Ring Hand C. O. Lamp.

Shell Footed C. O. Lam

Vine Footed C. O. Lamp.

Prism Lamp, C. O 5 in. Base.

Stedman C. O. Lamp 5 in. Base.

Vine C. O. Lamp, 5 in. Base.

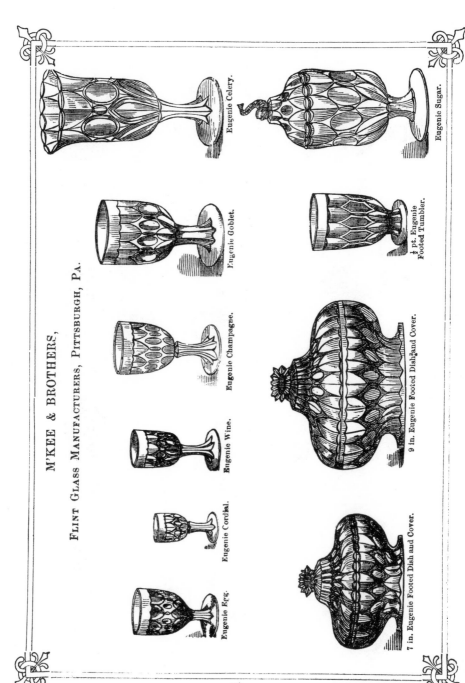

M'KEE & BROTHERS,

FLINT GLASS MANUFACTURERS, PITTSBURGH, PA.

Eugenie Celery.

Eugenie Sugar.

Eugenie Goblet.

½ pt. Eugenie Footed Tumbler.

Eugenie Champagne.

9 in. Eugenie Footed Dish and Cover.

Eugenie Wine.

Eugenie Cordial.

Eugenie Egg.

7 in. Eugenie Footed Dish and Cover.

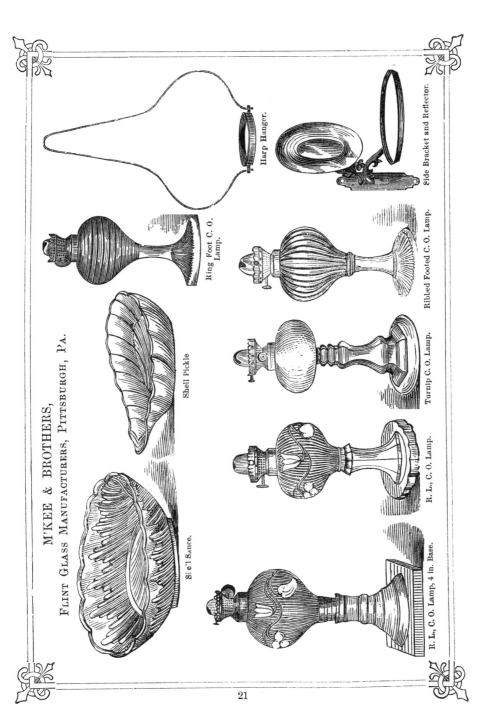

M'KEE & BROTHERS,
FLINT GLASS MANUFACTURERS, PITTSBURGH, PA.

Harp Hanger.

Side Bracket and Reflector.

Ring Foot C. O. Lamp.

Ribbed Footed C. O. Lamp.

Shell Pickle

Turnip C. O. Lamp.

R. L., C. O. Lamp.

Shell Sauce.

R. L., C. O. Lamp, 4 in. Base.

21

M'KEE & BROTHERS,

FLINT GLASS MANUFACTURERS, PITTSBURGH, PA.

Ray Sugar.

Temperance Tumbler.

Argus Ale.

⅓ qt. Band, foot Tumbler.

Mirror Tumbler.

⅓ qt. 10 Flute Ale.

Pony Tyrrell Ale. ½ pt. Steduan Tumbler.

6 flute Knob Ale.

½ pt. Steduan Tumbler.

Medium Tyrrell Ale.

½ pt. 9 Flute Tumbler.

½ pt. Tyrrell Ale.

Ray Celery.

½ pt. N. O. Bar Tumbler.

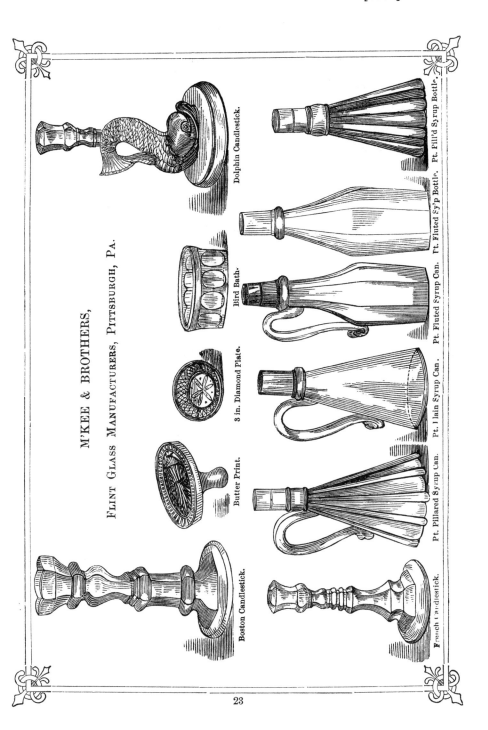

M'KEE & BROTHERS,

FLINT GLASS MANUFACTURERS, PITTSBURGH, PA.

Dolphin Candlestick.

Pt. Fill'd Syrup Bottle.

Pt. Fluted Sy'p Bottle.

Bird Bath.

Pt. Fluted Syrup Can.

3 in. Diamond Plate.

Pt. Plain Syrup Can.

Butter Print.

Pt. Pillared Syrup Can.

Boston Candlestick.

French Candlestick.

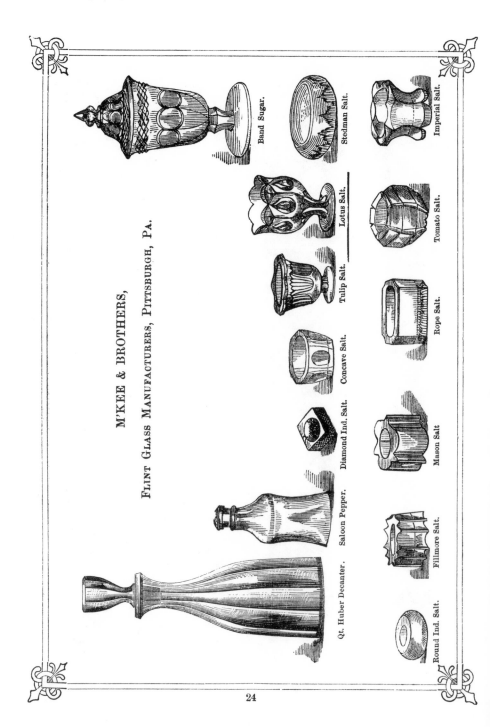

M'KEE & BROTHERS,
FLINT GLASS MANUFACTURERS, PITTSBURGH, PA.

Band Sugar.

Stedman Salt.

Imperial Salt.

Lotus Salt.

Tomato Salt.

Tulip Salt.

Rope Salt.

Concave Salt.

Diamond Ind. Salt.

Mason Salt.

Saloon Pepper.

Fillmore Salt.

Qt. Huber Decanter.

Round Ind. Salt.

M'KEE & BROTHERS,

FLINT GLASS MANUFACTURERS, PITTSBURGH, PA.

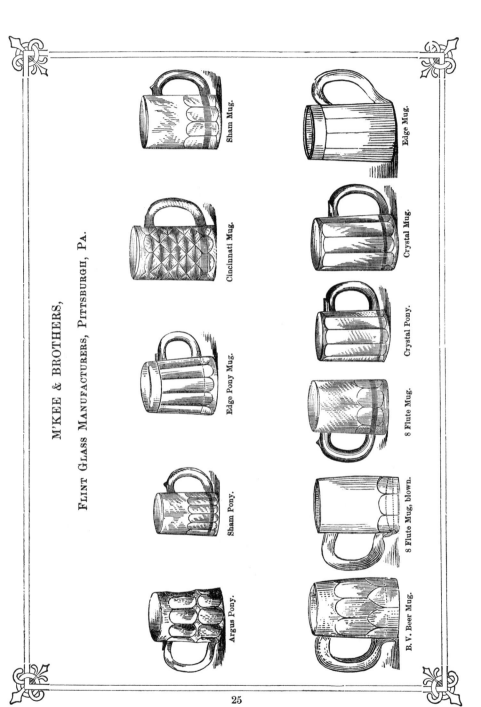

Sham Mug.

Edge Mug.

Cincinnati Mug.

Crystal Mug.

Edge Pony Mug.

Crystal Pony.

Sham Pony.

8 Flute Mug.

Argus Pony.

8 Flute Mug, blown.

B. V. Beer Mug.

M'Kee & Brothers, Flint Glass Manufacturers, Pittsburgh, Pa.

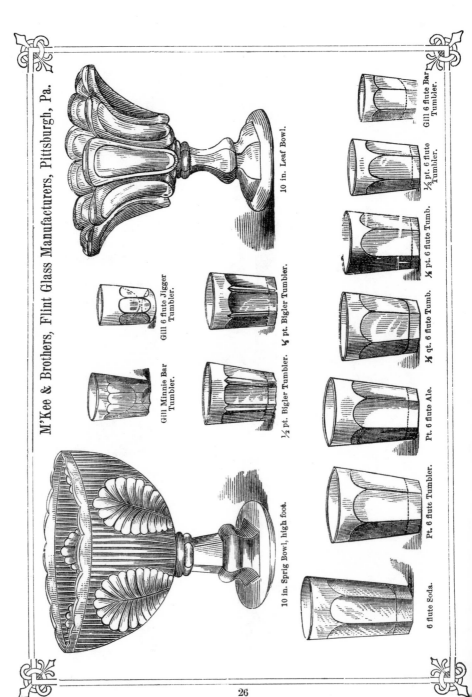

10 in. Leaf Bowl.

10 in. Sprig Bowl, high foot.

Gill 6 flute Jigger Tumbler.

Gill Minnie Bar Tumbler.

½ pt. Bigler Tumbler.

¼ pt. Bigler Tumbler.

Gill 6 flute Bar Tumbler.

⅓ pt. 6 flute Tumbler.

¼ pt. 6 flute Tumb.

½ qt. 6 flute Tumb.

¾ qt. 6 flute Tumb.

Pt. 6 flute Ale.

Pt. 6 flute Tumbler.

6 flute Soda.

M'KEE & BROTHERS,

Flint Glass Manufacturers, Pittsburgh.

9 in. Concave Bowl.

½ pt. 9 flute Bar Tumbler.

½ pt. 9 flute Bar Tumbler.

⅓ pt. Charleston Tumbler.

½ pt. Charleston Tumbler.

½ ½ pt Punch Tumbler.

⅓ qt. Punch Tumbler.

⅓ pt. Finger Flute Tumbler.

10 in. Scol. Diamond Bowl.

½ pt. Finger Flute Tumbler.

½ qt. Finger Flute Tumbler.

27

M'Kee & Brothers, Flint Glass Manufacturers, Pittsburgh, Pa.

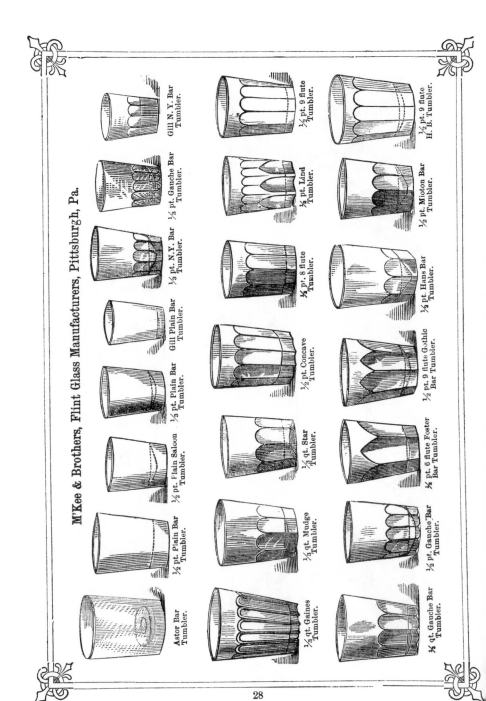

Astor Bar Tumbler.

½ pt. Plain Bar Tumbler.

½ pt. Plain Saloon Tumbler.

⅓ pt. Plain Bar Tumbler.

Gill Plain Bar Tumbler.

⅓ pt. N. Y. Bar Tumbler.

⅓ pt. Gauche Bar Tumbler.

Gill N. Y. Bar Tumbler.

¼ qt. Gaines Tumbler.

⅓ qt. Mudge Tumbler.

⅓ qt. Star Tumbler.

¼ pt. Concave Tumbler.

¾ pt. 8 flute Tumbler.

½ pt. Lind Tumbler.

½ pt. 9 flute Tumbler.

¼ qt. Gauche Bar Tumbler.

½ pt. Gauche Bar Tumbler.

½ pt. 6 flute Foster Bar Tumbler.

½ pt. 9 flute Gothic Bar Tumbler.

½ pt. Hans Bar Tumbler.

½ pt. Mioton Bar Tumbler.

½ pt. 9 flute H. B. Tumbler.

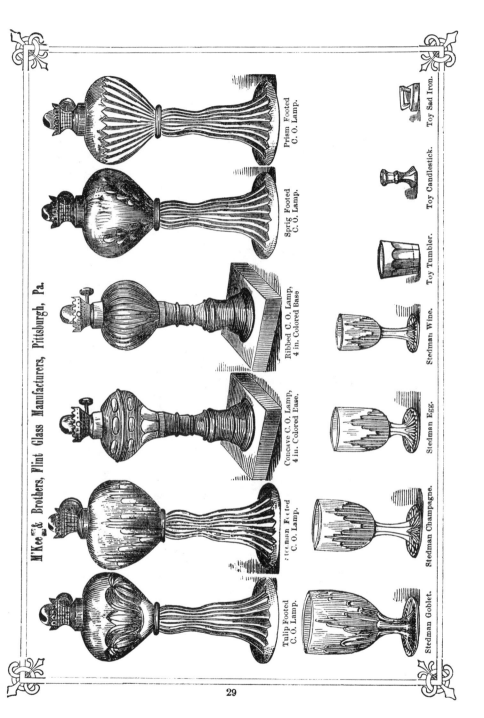

M'Kee & Brothers, Flint Glass Manufacturers, Pittsburgh, Pa.

Prism Footed C. O. Lamp.

Sprig Footed C. O. Lamp.

Ribbed C. O. Lamp, 4 in. Colored Base

Concave C. O. Lamp, 4 in. Colored Base.

Stedman Footed C. O. Lamp.

Tulip Footed C. O. Lamp.

Toy Sad Iron.

Toy Candlestick.

Toy Tumbler.

Stedman Wine.

Stedman Egg.

Stedman Champagne.

Stedman Goblet.

M'KEE & BROTHERS, FLINT GLASS MANUFACTURERS, PITTSBURGH, PA.

Shell C. O. Lamp, 5 in. Col. Base.

Sprig C. O. Lamp, 5 in. Col. Base

Turnip C. O. Lamp, 4 in. Col. Base

Argus C. O. Lamp, 4 in. Col. Base.

Tulip C. O. Lamp, 5 in. Colored Base.

7 in. Ray Nappy.

6 in. Ray Nappy.

7 in. Ray Dish.

9 in. Ray Dish.

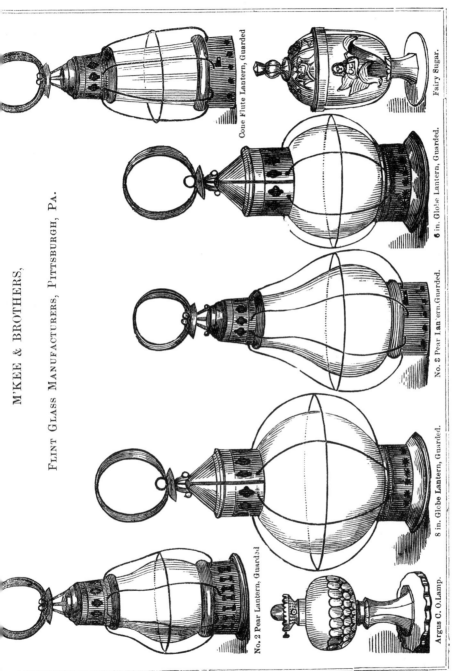

M'KEE & BROTHERS,

FLINT GLASS MANUFACTURERS, PITTSBURGH, PA.

Cone Flute Lantern, Guarded.

Fairy Sugar.

6 in. Globe Lantern, Guarded.

No. 3 Pear Lantern, Guarded.

8 in. Globe Lantern, Guarded.

No. 2 Pear Lantern, Guarded.

Argus C. O. Lamp.

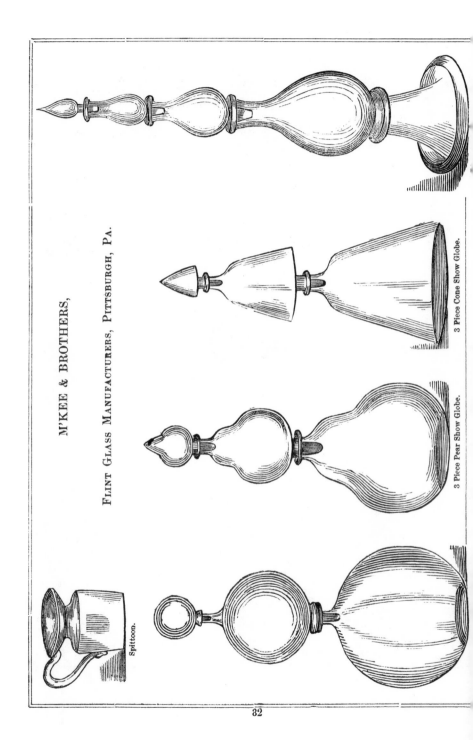

M'KEE & BROTHERS,

FLINT GLASS MANUFACTURERS, PITTSBURGH, PA.

Spittoon.

3 Piece Pear Show Globe.

3 Piece Cone Show Globe.

THE 1871 CATALOG

I N structure and approach the 1871 catalog follows the format of 1868. It emphasizes pressed tablewares but still shows a few pieces of the earlier standard patterns like Excelsior and Eugenie. The policy of featuring a single functional form is used again, although in that form there may be different designs and even different techniques. It is short, having only 24 pages, like the 1860 version.

Five patterns of pressed tableware received the full-page treatment. N.P.L. (New Pressed Leaf), introduced in 1868, covered two pages, with 16 pieces borrowed from the 1868 catalog. Three new patterns indicated the influence on glass firms of competition and the need to capture sales through novelty. Frosted, on two pages (20 pieces), indicates that the M'Kees had begun to use the hydrofluoric acid technique; Plain, the second new pattern, on two pages with 17 pieces, was just as revolutionary and certainly a reaction against the tradition of figured and geometric design. It would have been cheaper to produce, and it would lend itself well to etched decoration. It is not certain that M'Kee was the first house to make a plain pressed ware. In about 1875, King, Son & Co. named a plain pattern Mitchell A., B., C., D. and also used the name "Plain" in a set. M'Kee had used Plain for an undecorated blown creamer, bottles, and jars. The M'Kees also called an undecorated mold-blown molasses can Plain. The only application of Plain to pressed ware outside the tableware set was to unpatterned pressed tumblers.

The third new pressed tableware pattern was named Rustic. Gillinder of Philadelphia also offered a Rustic set. His pattern relates to a figural design appearing later than that of M'Kee. One whole page featured this pattern with nine pieces; four-fifths of another page shows ten pieces.

The fifth prominent tableware pattern was an old favorite—Crystal—two pages with 21 pieces. It is the only tableware pattern that remained popular from 1860 through 1871. Other pressed patterns appear but do not represent sets.

The 1871 catalog has five pages which are organized by function: tumblers, molasses cans (syrup cruets), mugs and stemware, lanterns, and show globes. The Rose molasses can had been dropped by 1871. Morton, the new can appearing in 1868, foretold the heaviness that characterized the eighties.

In 1861 J. B. Lyon made a Diamond molasses can almost like McKee's Diamond. He called it Star and Concave, the Star being contained within the Diamond and the Concave being a circle. The McKee Diamond has no figure within the diamond and the circle is somewhat elliptical.

Two exceptionally popular forms were ale and beer glasses. Only seven of these are shown in 1860 but there are 21 ale and beer glasses in 1864, 26 in 1868. Tumblers also appear in great variety in all of the catalogs. Many of the forms are so much alike that it is difficult for the observer to understand how a customer could have differentiated between them. There are soda tumblers, jelly tumblers, beer tumblers, ale tumblers, and numerous others. There are 29 tumblers in the 1860 catalog, and the number varies only slightly in all of the others. The separate category of bar tumblers is nearly as large. One assumes that the bar tumblers may have been a bit heavier. Though tumblers had various local names, the patterns consistently utilized the flute or a close likeness. The same generalization can be applied to patterned mugs. When 13 mugs appear on a single page one naturally thinks of beer. But the mugs are more important than that. The saloon had become an establishment, and glass of durable quality was advantageous and necessary.

We are not apt to think of Midwesterners of the sixties as being too concerned with the niceties of table setting or with the selection and serving of wine. We should realize, however, that Pittsburgh had over 86,000 people in 1870 and Allegheny County well over 100,000. Certainly the wealthy and traveled group understood wining and dining.

Probably many solid citizens could afford a whole set of glass tableware and were careful to use the stemware correctly. They could expect goblet, champagne, and wine in any large set. If they were particular, they could add cordial, claret, and footed ale. In the catalog advertisements an egg cup and a salt were often pictured with the stemware. By 1871, the word *cocktail* appears. In form, the clarets and cordials were very like wines. In the Eugenie pattern the cordial was smaller than the wine.

Two sorts of patterns decorated this stemware: major patterns that could be had in a whole set and other patterns manufactured only in a few popular pieces. In 1860, for instance, Crystal, Eugenie, and

Excelsior represented the set group, while Argus, Mioton, Mitre Diamond, Charleston, and H.S. might be complete in a few pieces. In 1864 the only incomplete stemware sets were New York and Mioton against the eight standard sets. In 1868 the ratio became four to six sets. Finally in 1871 six sets were represented, but only New York and Mioton were incomplete examples.

These four catalogs show clearly what was happening in tableware design. First, to fall back on a truism, good style is timeless. Crystal, as the M'Kees produced it, lasted throughout the 11 years. It is an undecorated panel or flute often reaching to the top of the piece. Obviously, Huber, Flute, Loop, and Leaf would be equally successful. Diamond, Mitre, and Scalloped Diamond also represent a permanent pattern.

Eugenie, Excelsior, and Ray typify the past. The heaviness-with-strength of cut glass is evident in Eugenie and Excelsior. Ray, borrowed from Lacy Glass, unfortunately lacked the brilliance and traditional unity of Eastern lacy. Its design is a cross between lacy and later pressed tableware.

An innovation in style had occurred in 1863–64 with the patenting of Sprig and the introduction of R.L. (Bellflower). Its distinctive quality, reeding, reached an apex in R.L. since the stylized Bellflower emphasized the reeding as a background better than the earlier Sprig. The design of reeding brought out patterns like Stedman and Prism. Even the bowls called Shell carry pillars like Stedman.

Competition forced glassmakers to seek novelty. No greater contrast to reeding could exist than Plain (undecorated). Frosted is half plain, a forerunner of etching and staining. Rustic, which uses a raised design, is also half-plain. The heavier part of the design near the top of the piece tapers toward the base so that the pattern seems top-heavy. If any of these patterns were produced in colored glass, no evidence exists in any of the catalogs. Apparently, the M'Kees did not manufacture colored tableware in sets in the 1860s, although single colored pieces in some of these patterns are occasionally found by collectors. From the 1864 catalog through the 1871, a collector would conclude that the late sixties were merely a transitional period before the true naturalistic designs arrived.

By 1871, the M'Kee Company had cut back its lamp production. Three candlesticks and the usual lanterns still appeared in the catalog, but the only lamps left were the suspension lamps for coal oil and the two hand lamps.

There are fewer celery vases than expected in all of the catalogs. Only three are shown in the 1860 catalog; four in 1863 and 1868 and 1871. In the 1871 catalog, none of the celery vases matched the sets of glassware, although they do in the early ones. Salts could be purchased to match a few of the patterns, but most of the salts offered by M'Kee did not match their pressed pattern glasses. By 1871, the number of salts was down to three, quite a drop in popularity from the previous decade.

The toy flatirons and candlesticks were still available in 1871 although they had disappeared by 1880, to be replaced by toy table sets. The Sundries and Household Wares were also available in 1871. These probably provided a bread-and-butter line for the M'Kee company.

Around the turn of the century, the M'Kee company made a much greater variety of patterns[16] It is interesting that in the sixties and seventies such a successful company made comparatively few patterns. Most of the older patterns had been completely dropped by 1880. Crystal was available in six shapes at that time and a few of the other patterns in one or two, but an almost completely new line had been introduced between 1871 and 1880. A new Brilliant pattern, quite different from that of 1864, and seven other new patterns available in sets were offered in 1880. Thus, the patterns we have been discussing, such as N.P.L. and Ray, were popular for little more than a decade.

PRICE VARIATIONS

Prices fluctuated quite a bit in the sixties. Most of the objects in these catalogs were sold by the dozen. Tomato salts were $1.60 a dozen in 1860 and in 1863. However, they had nearly doubled to $2.75 a dozen in 1864 but dropped slightly in 1868 to $2.50. Unfortunately, the 1871 catalog does not have a price list. The same pattern of raising and lowering prices is followed throughout the catalogs. The toys are listed at $2.70 a gross in 1860 and 1863, $4.75 a gross in 1864 and in 1868. Carbon oil lamps are $8.00 a dozen including chimneys in 1860; $4.00 a dozen with no chimney in 1863. They vary in price from $6.00 to $8.00 a dozen in 1864 and 1868. A goblet in Excelsior pattern was $1.90 a dozen in 1860, $1.67 in 1863, $3.50 in 1864, and then $3.00 a dozen in 1868. Bellflower goblets came into the catalog in 1863 at $2.00 a dozen, went up to $3.60 a dozen in 1864, and down to $2.67 a dozen in 1868. Tumblers were the cheapest items in the catalogs, varying from 60¢ to 93¢ a dozen in 1860, rising to a

[16] Stout, Sandra. *The Complete Book of McKee Glass*, North Kansas City: Trojan Press, 1972, pp. 46–96.

high of $1.33 and $2.00 a dozen for plain tumblers and bar tumblers in 1864, falling back to $1.25 for rough bottom tumblers and $1.80 for ground bottom ones.

These fluctuations in prices were general throughout the glass industry, probably because of inflation accompanying the Civil War. Prices rose steeply during the war until both prices and salaries had doubled by war's end. Then, as conditions stabilized, the lime formula was introduced, glass was more available, and prices dropped. During the sixties the glass industry experienced a major boom and virtually doubled its output.[17]

These four catalogs, covering a most important decade in the glass industry, reflect both the changing conditions in the industry and how a successful company like M'Kee trimmed its sails to fit the winds. We can note relationships to the products of competitors since Pittsburgh as a single area had more glass factories than any other American locality. The 11 years covered include the Civil War and its economic hardships. The development of the soda-lime formula, however, offset some of them by stimulating production. We have seen the introduction of large matching sets of glassware in the mid-1860s which gave the middle-class housewife something previously available only to the wealthy. The rise to prominence of kerosene as a lighting fluid created an expanding phase of glass manufacture.

Collectors and students, always fascinated by changing pattern styles, have fruitful opportunities in the pressed tableware designs. The traditional styles of cut glass faded into geometric figures and stylized forms. Then plain surfaces gradually prepared us for the naturalism, the color, and the frosting and etching of the seventies. Working on the catalogs was exciting, challenging, and taught us a valuable lesson: a catalog picture is only one documentation. We hope that collectors will find our comments helpful.

PICTURED IN THE 1871 CATALOG

PATTERN	NUMBER OF PIECES	PATTERN	NUMBER OF PIECES
Argus 1 —Type 2	1	Crystal	22
Boston candlestick	1	Diamond	2
Cincinnati	4	Diamond, Scalloped	1
Concave	2	Dolphin candlestick	1

[17] Davis, Pearce. *The Development of the American Glass Industry*, New York: Russell & Russell. 1949, pp. 118–120.

PATTERN	NUMBER OF PIECES	PATTERN	NUMBER OF PIECES
English, mo. can.	1	Stedman	2
Eugenie	2	Tomato	1
Eureka	6	Tulip	1
Excelsior	4		

MUGS (10)

Fillmore	1	Ashburton	2
Flute	9	Bismark	1
Flute, Broad	1	Flutes	3
French candlestick	1	Jarvis	1
Frosted	20	Milwaukee	1
Gaines	4	St. Louis	1
Huber	3	Sham	1

STEMWARE (4)

Imperial	1	
Leaf	1	California
Lotus	1	Continental
Mason	1	Greek cordial
Mioton	4	New Orleans cordial
Morton	1	

TUMBLERS (32)

New York	5	Charleston	1
N.P.L.	24	Flute	14
Pillared mo. can.	1	Janes	3
Plain	22	Jose	2
Prism mo. can.	1	Philadelphia	2
Ray	2	Plain	1
Ribbed	1	Sham	2
Ribbed, Fine	1	Smith	2
Ring	1	Taylor	1
Rustic	19	Tyrell	3
R.L.	3	Western	1
Rope	1	Also 21 not listed by name.
Shell	2		
Sprig	3		

ILLUSTRATED CATALOGUE

OF

MANUFACTURED BY

M'KEE & BROTHERS,

Wood Street, corner of Wood Street and First Avenue,

PITTSBURGH, PA.

PRINTED BY W. S. HAVEN & CO., CORNER WOOD STREET AND THIRD AVENUE.

1871.

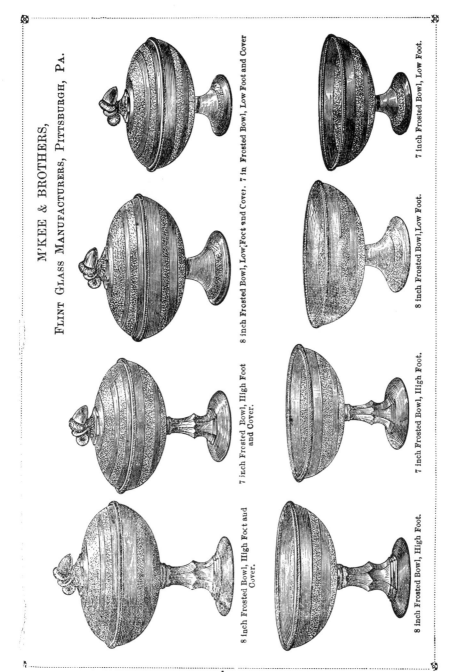

McKEE & BROTHERS,
FLINT GLASS MANUFACTURERS, PITTSBURGH, PA.

8 inch Frosted Bowl, Low Foot and Cover. 7 in Frosted Bowl, Low Foot and Cover

7 inch Frosted Bowl, Low Foot.

8 inch Frosted Bowl, Low Foot and Cover.

8 inch Frosted Bowl, Low Foot.

7 inch Frosted Bowl, High Foot and Cover.

7 inch Frosted Bowl, High Foot.

8 inch Frosted Bowl, High Foot and Cover.

8 inch Frosted Bowl, High Foot.

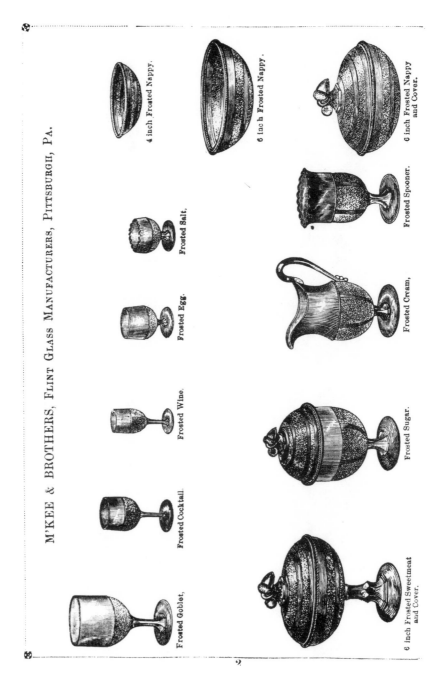

M'KEE & BROTHERS, FLINT GLASS MANUFACTURERS, PITTSBURGH, PA.

4 inch Frosted Nappy.

6 inch Frosted Nappy.

6 inch Frosted Nappy and Cover.

Frosted Salt.

Frosted Spooner.

Frosted Egg.

Frosted Cream,

Frosted Wine.

Frosted Cocktail.

Frosted Sugar.

Frosted Goblet,

6 inch Frosted Sweetmeat and Cover.

M'KEE & BROTHERS,

FLINT GLASS MANUFACTURERS, PITTSBURGH, PA.

6 inch Ray Plate.

6 inch R. L. Plate.

6 in. Sprig Plate.

Eureka Cordial.

Eureka Egg.

Eureka Wine.

Eureka Champagne.

Eureka Ft. Tumbler.

Eureka Goblet.

N. Y. Egg.

N. Y. Ale.

N. Y. Wine.

N. Y. Champagne.

N. Y. Goblet

McKEE & BROTHERS, FLINT GLASS MANUFACTURERS, PITTSBURGH, PA.

8 inch Rustic Bowl, low foot.

6 inch Rustic Nappie and cover.

8 inch Rustic Bowl, low foot and cover.

Rustic Spooner.

Rustic Cream.

8 inch Rustic Bowl, high foot.

Rustic Sugar.

8 in. Rustic Bowl, high foot and cover.

6 in. Rustic Sweetmeat and Cover.

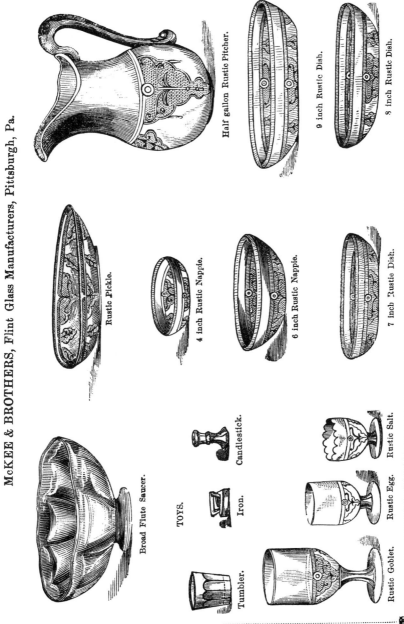

McKEE & BROTHERS, Flint Glass Manufacturers, Pittsburgh, Pa.

Half gallon Rustic Pitcher.

9 inch Rustic Dish.

8 inch Rustic Dish.

Rustic Pickle.

4 inch Rustic Napple.

6 inch Rustic Napple.

7 inch Rustic Dish.

Broad Flute Saucer.

TOYS.

Candlestick.

Iron.

Tumbler.

Rustic Salt.

Rustic Egg.

Rustic Goblet.

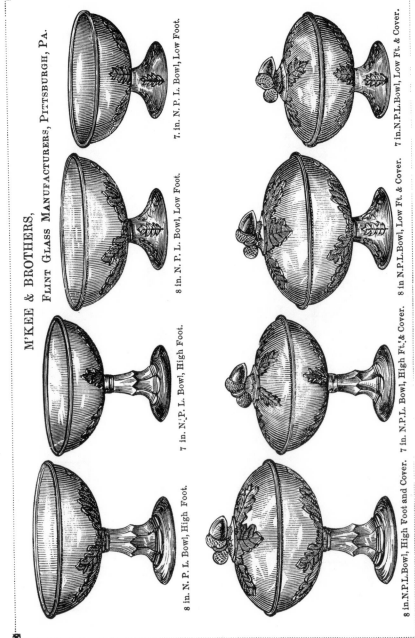

M'KEE & BROTHERS,

FLINT GLASS MANUFACTURERS, PITTSBURGH, PA.

7 in. N. P. L. Bowl, Low Foot.

8 in. N. P. L. Bowl, Low Foot.

7 in. N. P. L. Bowl, High Foot.

8 in. N. P. L. Bowl, High Foot.

7 in. N.P.L.Bowl, Low Ft. & Cover.

8 in N.P.L.Bowl, Low Ft. & Cover.

7 in. N.P.L. Bowl, High Ft. & Cover.

8 in. N.P.L.Bowl, High Foot and Cover.

M'KEE & BROTHERS, FLINT GLASS MANUFACTURERS, PITTSBURGH, PA.

½ gal. N. P. L. Pitcher.

4 in. N. P. L. Nappy.

N. P. L. Egg.

N. P. L. Wine.

N. P. L. Claret.

N. P. L. Champagne.

N. P. L. Goblet.

7 in. N. P. L. Dish.

8 in. N. P. L. Dish.

9 in. N. P. L. Dish.

N. P. L. Salt.

6 in. N. P. L. Nappie & Cover.

N. P. L. Spooner.

N. P. L. Cream.

N. P. L. Sugar.

6 in. N. P. L. Sweetmeat & Cover.

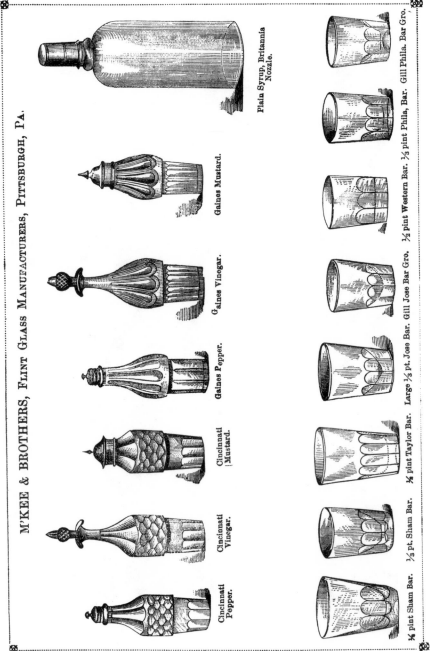

M'KEE & BROTHERS, Flint Glass Manufacturers, Pittsburgh, Pa.

Plain Syrup, Britannia Nozzle.

Gaines Mustard.

Gaines Vinegar.

Gaines Pepper.

Cincinnati Mustard.

Cincinnati Vinegar.

Cincinnati Pepper.

Gill Phila. Bar Gro.

½ pint Phila, Bar.

½ pint Western Bar.

Gill Jose Bar Gro.

Large ⅓ pt. Jose Bar. Gill Jose Bar.

¾ pint Taylor Bar.

⅓ pt. Sham Bar.

¾ pint Sham Bar.

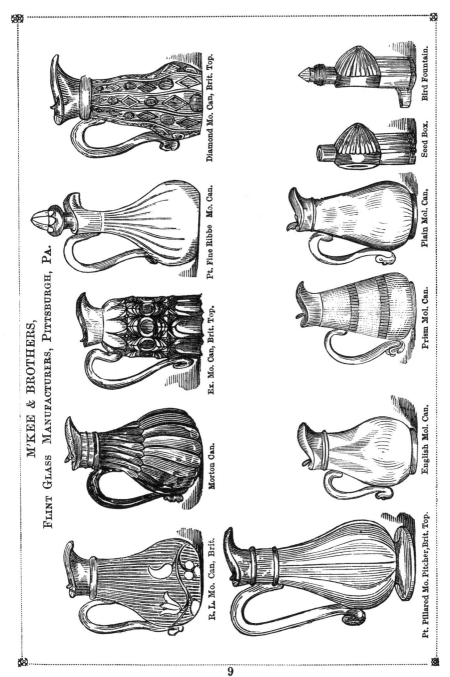

M'KEE & BROTHERS,

FLINT GLASS MANUFACTURERS, PITTSBURGH, PA.

Diamond Mo. Can, Brit. Top.

Bird Fountain.

Seed Box.

Pt. Fine Ribbe   Mo. Can.

Plain Mol. Can,

Ex. Mo. Can, Brit. Top.

Prism Mol. Can.

Morton Can.

English Mol. Can.

R. L. Mo. Can, Brit.

Pt. Pillared Mo. Pitcher, Brit. Top.

M'KEE & BROTHERS,

Flint Glass Manufacturers, Pittsburgh, Pa

10 in. Crystal Bowl.

Crystal Spoonholder.

Crystal Cream.

Crystal Ale.

Qt. Crystal Pitcher.

8 in. Crystal Dish, footed and Cover.

Crystal Celery.

8 in. Crystal Bowl.

Crystal Sugar.

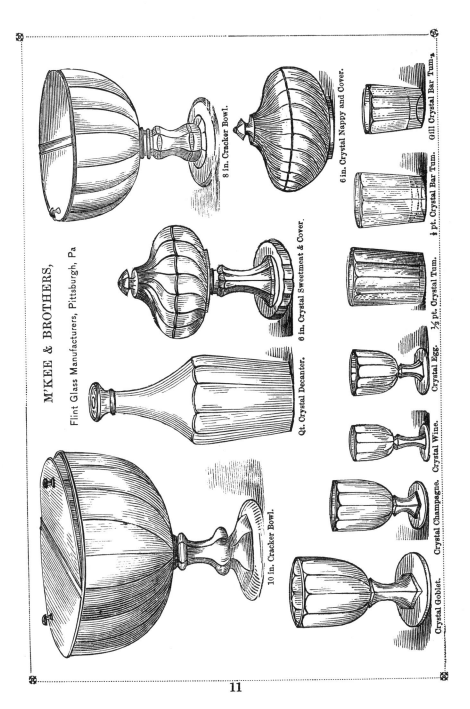

M'KEE & BROTHERS,

Flint Glass Manufacturers, Pittsburgh, Pa

8 in. Cracker Bowl.

6 in. Crystal Nappy and Cover.

Gill Crystal Bar Tum.

¼ pt. Crystal Bar Tum.

6 in. Crystal Sweetmeat & Cover.

½ pt. Crystal Tum.

Qt. Crystal Decanter.

Crystal Egg.

Crystal Wine.

10 in. Cracker Bowl.

Crystal Champagne.

Crystal Goblet.

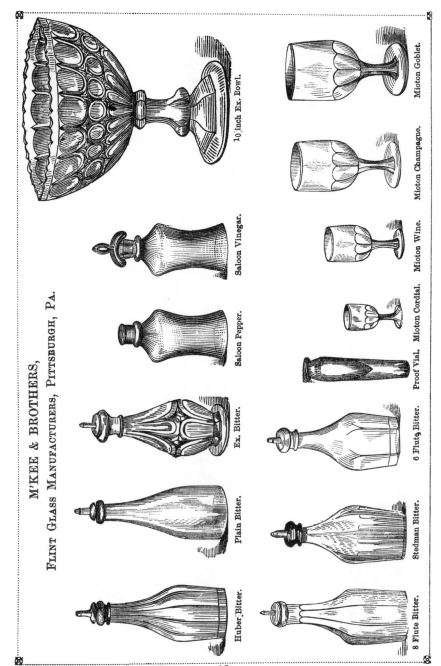

M'KEE & BROTHERS,
FLINT GLASS MANUFACTURERS, PITTSBURGH, PA.

10 inch Ex. Bowl.

Saloon Vinegar.

Saloon Pepper.

Ex. Bitter.

Plain Bitter.

Huber Bitter.

Mioton Goblet.

Mioton Champagne.

Mioton Wine.

Mioton Cordial.

Proof Vial.

6 Flute Bitter.

Stedman Bitter.

8 Flute Bitter.

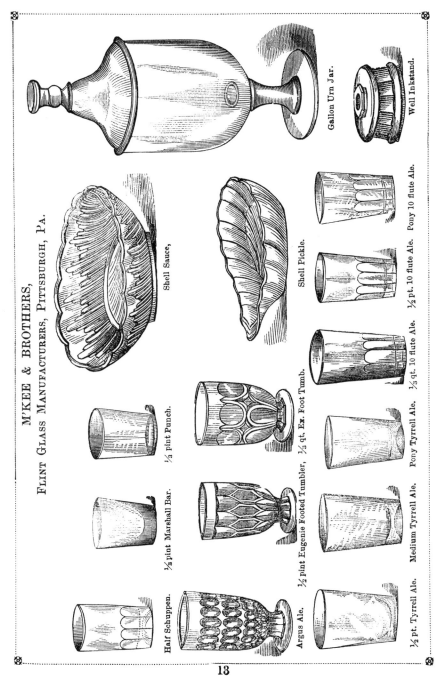

M'KEE & BROTHERS,
FLINT GLASS MANUFACTURERS, PITTSBURGH, PA.

Gallon Urn Jar.

Well Inkstand.

Shell Sauce,

Shell Pickle.

Pony 10 flute Ale.

½ pt. 10 flute Ale.

⅓ qt. 10 flute Ale.

⅓ pint Punch.

⅓ qt. Ex. Foot Tumb.

Pony Tyrrell Ale.

½ pint Marshall Bar.

½ pint Eugenie Footed Tumbler,

Medium Tyrrell Ale.

Half Schuppen.

Argus Ale.

½ pt. Tyrrell Ale.

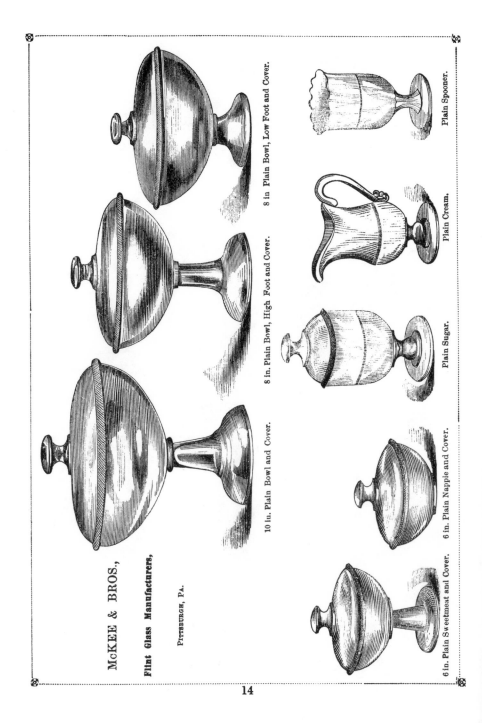

McKEE & BROS.,

Flint Glass Manufacturers,

PITTSBURGH, PA.

8 in. Plain Bowl, Low Foot and Cover.

8 in. Plain Bowl, High Foot and Cover.

10 In. Plain Bowl and Cover.

Plain Spooner.

Plain Cream.

Plain Sugar.

6 in. Plain Nappie and Cover.

6 in. Plain Sweetmeat and Cover.

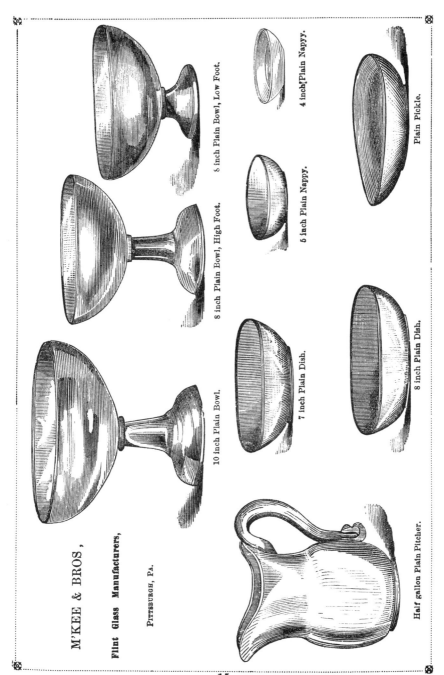

M'KEE & BROS,

Flint Glass Manufacturers,

PITTSBURGH, PA.

10 inch Plain Bowl.

8 inch Plain Bowl, High Foot.

8 inch Plain Bowl, Low Foot.

5 inch Plain Nappy.

4 inch Plain Nappy.

Plain Pickle.

7 inch Plain Dish.

8 inch Plain Dish.

Half gallon Plain Pitcher.

M'KEE & BROTHERS,
FLINT GLASS MANUFACTURERS, PITTSBURGH, PA.

Plain Goblet.

Plain Egg.   Plain Wine.   Plain Cocktail.

Huber Celery.

Eugenie Celery.

Ray Celery.

Bird Bath.

8 in. Diamond Plate.

Butter Print.

Boston Candlestick.

Dolphin Candlestick.

French Candlestick.

Ribb'd Hand C. O. Lamp.

Ring Hand C. O. Lamp.

M'Kee & Brothers, Flint Glass Manufacturers, Pittsburgh, Pa.

¼ gall. Sprig Pitcher.

¼ gall. Ring Jar.

Qt. Tincture.

Qt. Specimen Bottle.

½ gall. R. L. Pitcher.

Side Bracket and Reflector.

Small Suspension C. O. Lamp.

Large Suspension C. O. Lamp.

½ gall. Squat Jar.

¼ gall. Specie Jar.

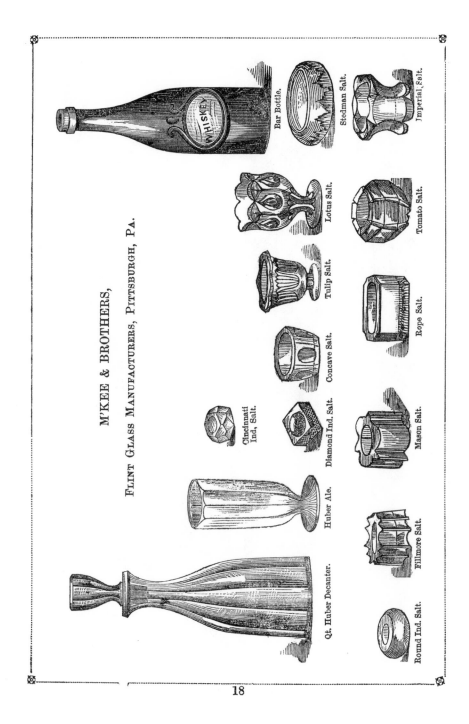

M'KEE & BROTHERS,

FLINT GLASS MANUFACTURERS, PITTSBURGH, PA.

Bar Bottle.

Stedman Salt.

Imperial Salt.

Lotus Salt.

Tomato Salt.

Tulip Salt.

Rope Salt.

Concave Salt.

Cincinnati Ind. Salt.

Diamond Ind. Salt.

Mason Salt.

Huber Ale.

Fillmore Salt.

Qt. Huber Decanter.

Round Ind. Salt.

M'KEE & BROTHERS, FLINT GLASS MANUFACTURERS, PITTSBURGH, PA.

Continental Goblet.

Crystal Catawba.

Ex-Jelly.

California Wine.

New Orleans Cordial.

Plain Footed Ale.

Greek Cordial.

Milwaukee Mug.

Bismarck Mug.

Sham Pony.

Jarvis Mug.

St. Louis Mug.

Ashburton Pony.

Ashburton Mng

Huber Mug.

Crystal Mug.

Crystal Pony.

8 Flute Mug.

8 Flute Pony.

Short Flute Mug.

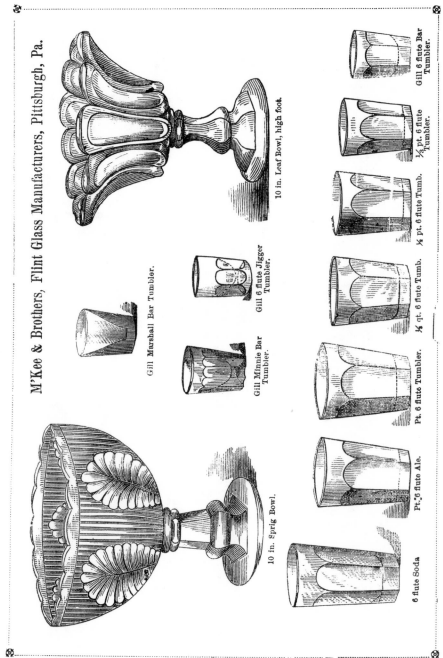

M'Kee & Brothers, Flint Glass Manufacturers, Pittsburgh, Pa.

10 in. Leaf Bowl, high foot.

Gill Marshall Bar Tumbler.

Gill 6 flute Jigger Tumbler.

Gill Minnie Bar Tumbler.

10 in. Sprig Bowl.

6 flute Soda

Pt. 6 flute Ale.

Pt. 6 flute Tumbler.

½ qt. 6 flute Tumb.

¼ qt. 6 flute Tumb.

½ pt. 6 flute Tumb.

⅓ pt. 6 flute Tumbler.

Gill 6 flute Bar Tumbler.

M'KEE & BROTHERS,
Flint Glass Manufacturers, Pittsburgh.

9 in. Concave Bowl.

⅓ pt. Smith.

½ pt. Smith.

Crimped Soda.

Plain Soda.

½ pt. Charleston Tumbler.

¼ pt. Janes.

½ pt. Janes.

10 in. Scol. Diamond Bowl.

⅓ qt. Janes.

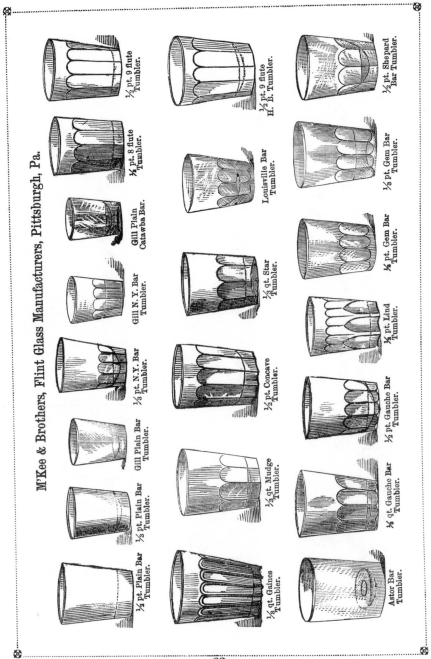

McKee & Brothers, Flint Glass Manufacturers, Pittsburgh, Pa.

½ pt. 9 flute Tumbler.
⅓ pt. 8 flute Tumbler.
Gill Plain Catawba Bar.
Gill N. Y. Bar Tumbler.
⅓ pt. N. Y. Bar Tumbler.
Gill Plain Bar Tumbler.
⅓ pt. Plain Bar Tumbler.
½ pt. Plain Bar Tumbler.

½ pt. 9 flute H. B. Tumbler.
Louisville Bar Tumbler.
⅓ qt. Star Tumbler.
½ pt. Concave Tumbler.
⅓ qt. Mudge Tumbler.
⅓ qt. Gaines Tumbler.

½ pt. Shepard Bar Tumbler.
⅓ pt. Gem Bar Tumbler.
⅓ pt. Gem Bar Tumbler.
⅓ pt. Lind Tumbler.
½ pt. Gauche Bar Tumbler.
⅓ qt. Gauche Bar Tumbler.
Astor Bar Tumbler.

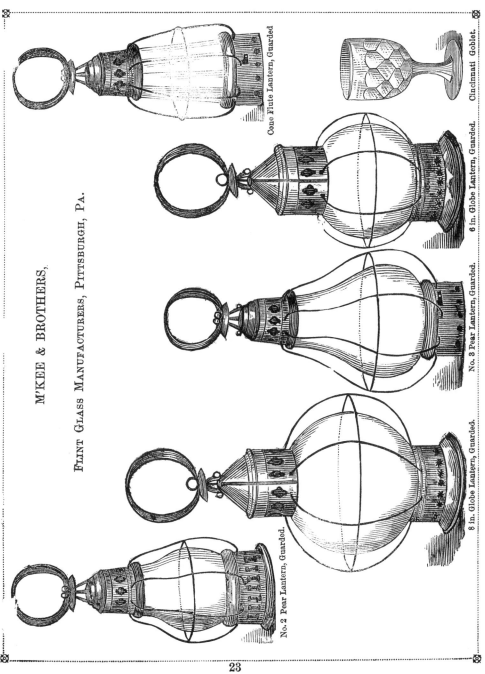

M'KEE & BROTHERS,

FLINT GLASS MANUFACTURERS, PITTSBURGH, PA.

Cone Flute Lantern, Guarded.

Cincinnati Goblet.

6 in. Globe Lantern, Guarded.

No. 3 Pear Lantern, Guarded.

No. 2 Pear Lantern, Guarded.

8 in. Globe Lantern, Guarded.

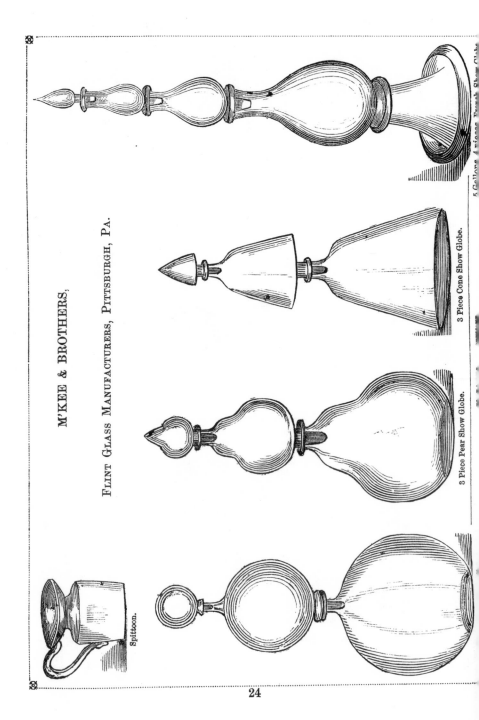

M'KEE & BROTHERS,

FLINT GLASS MANUFACTURERS, PITTSBURGH, PA.

Spittoon.

3 Piece Pear Show Globe.

3 Piece Cone Show Globe.